Red Flight, Break!

By

Roger Maxim

THE DECISION

There I was, in an airplane 5000 feet above the Texas plains. It was a new perspective for me and I was quite the sightseer. The Instructor's voice broke into my pastoral reverie telling me to pull the nose up abruptly. "Throttle to idle and stick hard back!" That's what he said. *O.K.,* I thought, *I'll do what I'm told.* The plane started to climb ever more slowly. Just before we seemed to stop flying, he ordered "Hard right rudder!" I didn't see how that would do anything because we were very nearly stopped in mid-air. Suddenly I found out!!

In an instant, the nose of the airplane was pointed straight down and the world was spinning crazily. The earth was coming closer with frightening speed. That's when the thought hit me: *Holy cow! I'm supposed to be FLYING this airplane!*

* * * * * * * * * *

It all started at a Saturday matinee. Kate, my girl-friend-of-the-moment, was getting her hair done in preparation for our June, 1942 graduation from Oklahoma A&M in Stillwater, Oklahoma. To kill time, I went to the movies. The first movie was a forgettable western set in the 1870's featuring a toothy star and a surprisingly 1942-looking female lead. Intermission, which I usually ignored, featured a just-released short film. That film changed my life. Familiar actor Jimmy Stewart climbed out of an airplane and starred in a recruiting film called "Winning Your Wings." Jimmy, in his winsome "aw shucks" manner, extolled the excitement of joining the Army Air Force. Prestige, pay, and pretty girls, all while serving to keep our country free. An enticing mix!

I was graduating in few days with a degree in Engineering and I had been thinking about "What next?", but I hadn't made any firm decision. Naturally, thoughts of joining the military were prominent, but which branch and what job were not clear in my mind. Jimmy's smile and enthusiastic approach made my mind up for me.

I left the theater and, because Kate hadn't appeared yet, took myself over to the Army recruiting office to find out about what Jimmy Stewart had said. If what he said was right, I expected I would sign some papers and be in the Army Air Force. I was not yet aware of the "military way" of doing things...

The middle-aged man inside, looking sharp in his well-fitted olive drab uniform, greeted me with a smile.

"Hello, young man. Looking to join up?"

"Well, yes, I guess I am. I want to be a pilot!"

He grinned. "Ah. You've seen Jimmy Stewart's new recruiting film, eh? It just came out."

I nodded.

"Well, son, to become a pilot in the United States Army Air Force is not as easy as signing up for your class in English Lit. First of all, how old are you?"

"Twenty-one."

"Finish college yet?"

"I graduate this coming Thursday."

He nodded in approval. "Good. What's your major?"

"Engineering."

That brought a smile. "Even better," he paused, "Have you participated in any sports?"

4

"Yes. I lettered Varsity swim team for two years and Varsity baseball for three years."

"Baseball, eh. You fellas didn't have such a great season this year, did you?"

Much to my embarrassment, he was correct.

"Well, no, we didn't do all that great this year. Last year, under Coach Iba, we were 8 and 2. This year though, with Coach Greene being new, and some of the guys already left for the service, we were only 6 and 5."

He again nodded. "Well, my friend, you seem to be qualified to apply, but you'll have to provide some documents, and don't skip any because they're all important." He gave me a list:

1. Properly filled out application form, supported by three letters of recommendation from citizens of prominence in your place of domicile.
2. Legal evidence of place and date of birth.
3. A registrar's certificate of college or university credits.

I was very fortunate that I happened to have all of the documents, or could get them quickly. I could use the letters of recommendation from my college application and I had a certified copy of my birth certificate. The only new one was the registrar's certificate. No problem, though. I was sure Mrs. Gallagher in the Registrar's office could give me a formal transcript of my grades.

I described all this and he responded by opening his desk drawer and bringing out an official application form which he handed to me.

"O.K, son, take this with you and complete it very carefully. Add your other papers with it so they're ready to submit. Now, you mentioned how lucky you are to have the documents handy—but you're luckier than you think. Next Saturday morning, there will arrive here a large van

5

emblazoned with aviation cadet advertising on its side. You can't miss it. That van is a traveling aviation cadet examining board. They will examine your application and papers, conduct a detailed interview, and give you a physical exam right there in the van. If all goes well, they'll swear you in and start your processing."

"Where will they be?"

He responded; "At the curb right in front of this office. I'd suggest you be here no later than 7AM."

I thanked him and left. As I exited the office and turned up Monroe Street, I saw Kate coming out of the beauty parlor.

"Hi, Kate. Are you all finished?"

"Yes. How do you like my new hairdo?"

Actually, I didn't like it very much. It looked to me like a bowl of frizz. But I also knew better than to say so.

"Oh, it looks—nice."

"Nice? That's all, just "nice"?

"Sure. I mean it's—fine. You look nice."

The hurt expression told it all. "I'm sorry you don't like it, but it's the latest rage. *I* like it!"

I tried to think fast. "Well, that's what really counts, isn't it? Besides, what do I know—I'm a guy! And you really do look fine!"

That seemed to placate her.

"So," she said, somewhat distractedly, "what did you do while I was busy?"

"I joined the Air Force."

"How nice. You won't believe what the hairdresser said about Mary Jane..." She suddenly stopped in mid-sentence. "You did <u>what</u>!?"

I smiled. "I joined the Army Air Force. Or, at least, I have all the papers so I can join. I'll get officially signed up the Saturday after graduation."

"Tommy Peters, have you lost your mind!? Besides, you know I don't date servicemen."

I couldn't help but laugh. "Kate, pretty soon, ALL of the guys will be servicemen. Then you won't have anyone to date at all!"

This caused her a moment's pause. "Well," she finally spluttered, "I guess I'll have to deal with that later! Good bye, Tommy Peters, have fun zooming around the sky!"

With that, Kate flounced right out of my life. Strangely, I felt rather unaffected by it.

"I SWEAR..."

Graduation was held Thursday afternoon and my parents described it as "very nice." Actually, I thought it was rather tedious, except when they called my name, of course. More fun was the graduation dance held Thursday evening. Dancing the night away with various female classmates was certainly "very nice." Interestingly, Kate avoided me, not to my surprise. That brief chapter was certainly closed.

My life became very interesting Saturday morning, though. I appeared at the recruiting office fifteen minutes before the suggested 7:00 AM and I was glad I did. When I arrived, there was already a line of about fifteen other guys. By the time I left later in the day, the line numbered over fifty!

When it was my turn to enter the van, I handed my papers to a soldier with a golden chevron having two stripes on his sleeve. He checked my papers very carefully, and then handed me a card to complete, which he called the "qualification card." Next, I was put at a counter and given a test called the "AGCT", which was similar to the several intelligence and aptitude tests I'd taken in school. Afterward, I was told I had scored 147, and that seemed to be a good score. Next came a mechanical aptitude test, which I thought was easy, and my score was 121. Finally, there was a radio code aptitude test, which I did NOT enjoy, but I guess I did OK. All of my scores were entered on my qualification card. I was then directed to a man who conducted a fairly in-depth interview relating to my interests, experience, and past jobs, and he especially zeroed-in on my experience with airplanes.

"Mr. Peters, have you ever flown or flown in an airplane?"

"No, sir."

"Do you have any experience with or exposure to airplanes?"

"Yes, sir." I thought back to my childhood fascination with flying machines. "I have been fascinated by flying since the first time I ever looked up and saw an airplane. I have been around airplanes many times at air shows and displays. I have often thought how I would love to be able to fly."

"I see. But you didn't take advantage of the civilian pilot training offered by your college?"

Uh, oh, I thought, *I guess I should have joined when I had the chance...*

"Well, sir, I was aware of the program, but I was so deeply into my studies I didn't feel I had time. That and sports. I guess I'm a pretty competitive guy."

"I see. Well, as I review your scores, you certainly display the intelligence and aptitudes the Army Air Force is seeking. I will recommend you for air crew training. Now please join the line there in the rear of the van to receive your preliminary physical exam."

Well, I seem to have done all right. I guess 'air crew training' includes pilots. At least the physical shouldn't be a problem.

Indeed, the physical wasn't a problem. No color blindness, good depth perception, visual acuity of 20/15. Overall physical condition marked "excellent". All was duly noted on my card. I was then directed to a man with two silver bars on his shoulder.

"Mr. Peters, you have displayed the intelligence and aptitudes to qualify you for service in the United States Army Air Force. You have been accepted for air crew training which includes the positions of pilot, bombardier, or navigator. When I administer the oath of service, you will enter the Army as an enlisted grade Aviation Cadet. You will be sent to the processing center at Kelly Field, near San Antonio, Texas for further in-depth testing and processing. Do you wish to proceed?"

I must have smiled.

"I'm glad to see you are enthusiastic about becoming a member of our service." He then stood.

"Please stand."

I stood.

"Raise your right hand and repeat after me:"

He stated the oath from memory, pausing every few words so I could repeat the words exactly.

"I, Thomas J. Peters, do solemnly swear that I will support and defend the Constitution of the United States against all enemies, foreign and domestic; that I will bear true faith and allegiance to the same; and that I will obey the orders of the President of the United States and the orders of the officers appointed over me, according to regulations and the Articles of War, So help me God."

"You may lower your hand. Welcome to the United States Army Air Force!"

He handed me a manila envelope with my name and other information lettered on it. Inside were all of my papers and the all-important qualification card. "Do not lose this envelope! This is the most important set of documents you will ever have in the Army!"

He looked at a list on his desk and seemed rather surprised at what he saw. "Hmmm, I expected a delay in entry due to the vast numbers of new recruits being processed, but you hit a gap and will go immediately." Then he looked at me and stated, "Report back here to the recruiting office at 0700 Monday morning. You will be given your transportation tickets and further directions."

We shook hands and he eased me out the door.

Monday morning was rather chaotic. There were, by my count, fifty-seven of us, all newly-enlisted Aviation Cadets. I knew many of the other fellows from college and, as we milled around talking, it seemed the others were as nervous as I was.

Finally, the recruiter stepped outside. "OK, fellows, listen up!"

We were all eager to learn our directions.

"You have all been sworn in and are now members of the Army Air Force. This is a proud and elite organization, so don't do anything to smear our reputation! We seem to have a lucky charm among us." He smiled. "Aviation Cadet Peters was telling me how lucky he was. Well, his luck seems to hold. You fellows are being sent immediately to the processing station. There are hundreds of others who are not so lucky. They are sitting at home, awaiting their orders. Sometimes waiting for months. You see, the Air Force is filling up faster than we can process everyone. But you fellows hit just the right timing and you can be run through immediately. Good luck, indeed!"

He went on to tell us how to get where we were going and what to do when we first arrived.

"I want somebody to be in charge while you're in transit, so—Peters, that's you. Use your luck to get everyone to San An-tone in one piece."

I was stunned, and somewhat embarrassed, but all I could do was nod in agreement. He then called each man's name and gave him his train ticket and something he called a "chit" that would pay for our meals.

11

"OK, men, your train leaves at 10:30 AM. Get on over to the station and—good luck!"

CLASSIFICATION

The train trip went fine and my first exercise in leadership was a non-event. The other guys were too excited about starting our training to cause trouble, and we spent most of our time either talking with old friends, getting acquainted with new friends, or sleeping.

Our train's arrival at San Antonio that evening was just a little late, but there were Air Force people there to gather us up and get us loaded into the back of what I always thought of as an "army truck." I learned such trucks are not comfortable. I was also shocked by how many other men had arrived from all over the middle of the United States. There were hundreds of recruits just like us. Something else I noticed—military orders seem always to be shouted loudly and sternly. Apparently, there is nowhere in the military lexicon for "please" and "thank you"! We eventually bounced and jarred our way to the main gate of Kelly Field, where we were all shouted and ordered into lines and marched onto the base.

We lined up in front of a long, two-story wooden building. Then the speech started. But it was actually very interesting and I learned a lot.

"Welcome to the Cadet Processing Center, Kelly Field, Texas."

I think we all know we're in Texas, I thought wryly to myself.

"You will spend the next three weeks undergoing many tests both physical and mental, to determine what job you are suited for in the Air Force. At the end of testing, you will be assigned to training as either a pilot, navigator, or bombardier. You do have an opportunity to express your preference but, ultimately, your scores and the needs of the service will determine your final suitability. If you fail to meet the required qualifications for air crew training, you will be transferred to other suitable duties within the United States Army."

Hmmm, I thought, *there's no guarantee I'll be a pilot. But that's what I want to do, so I guess I'd better do my best at all of whatever they have me do...*

"You will be the last group processed here at Kelly Field. We are severely overcrowded and a new processing base is nearly finished adjacent to Kelly. That means you will be in very crowded conditions. First, listen up for your training company assignment."

He called all our names and assigned us to Company A, B, C, or D. I was in Company C.

"Now, when I release you, go into the barracks I indicate. Company A into the barracks right behind us, on the ground floor. Company B, same barracks, upstairs. Company C to the next barracks to left, on the ground floor. Company D same barracks, upstairs. When you are dismissed, go to your assigned barracks and find an empty bunk. Remain in the barracks until lights out at 2130. Get some sleep and report back here in front of the barracks at 0530 tomorrow morning and form up by companies. You are dismissed."

"Crowded" was an understatement! The bunks were placed so close together that there was hardly room to stand. There were lines of guys in the bathroom at the urinals and toilets. It looked like if I wanted a shower, I'd have to take it at midnight. Oh, well—welcome to the Army!

Up until then, what I'd experienced wasn't all that different from my experiences in high school and college

14

sports. The barked orders, the crowds of guys, etc. But that next morning, things changed dramatically. We were lined up, taught how to stand at attention, taught what "At Ease" meant, and told that when ordered to march, you started with your left foot. We then received our first formal marching orders and we headed for breakfast. To my eye, we looked like a rag-tag bunch of civilians straggling along.

After a luxurious 15 minutes to wolf down what we all came to know "SOS", which was actually creamed chipped beef on toast, we began a day that we would all remember as long as we lived.

First, we marched off to the base barbershop where they buzzed off all our hair. I normally wore my hair fairly short, but some of the guys who favored long, swept-back styles were quite chagrined to see their flowing locks in a pile on the floor! And for a while, it was hard to recognize who was who. Next, we marched (sort of) to a warehouse where we were issued our uniforms. Although this was serious business, there was a sense of hilarity at the clothing issue. We passed before a line of clerks who issued us our clothes, based entirely upon their guess as to our size. Some were pretty close, but others were really funny. The tall guys whose utility pants stopped at the top of their ankles. The little guys, whose pants trailed a foot or more on the floor. It was like a scene from a comedy movie. I guess we needed the laughter as a way to relax our increasingly jangled nerves, because our leaders let us laugh. After a lot of trading, everyone ended up with a workable set of uniform pieces. We then packed up our civilian clothes in thoughtfully provided cardboard boxes and addressed them to home. You're in the Army now!

There are certain highlights that come to mind of those three busy weeks. For example, I was intrigued by the amazing test devices used to test our coordination, balance, finger dexterity, and strength. For example, the machine that was sort of like a giant gyroscope that we climbed into and were twisted and turned through all sorts of gyrations to test our balance and balance recovery. When we each climbed out after our turn, some of the guys staggered, some of the guys fell, and one of the fellows threw up. I staggered a bit, but I thought it was fun! Our performance was not just observed, it was scientifically measured. Fascinating! Our meetings with the psychologist were also interesting, mainly because I thought it was a bunch mumbo-jumbo. But the AAF seemed to find it helpful. We also marched, marched, marched. Our group actually became pretty good at it and we took pride in being better than the others.

All of these results were compiled for each of us in what were called "Stanines". The term was coined from the words "STAndard NINE," and referred to the aptitude rating given each man on a scale that ranged from one to nine. A stanine of nine meant an individual was among those in the top scoring category on tests that predicted probability of success in the specialty for which the stanine was determined; a score of five meant he was in a group scoring in the middle category; a score of one placed him in the lowest category of scorers. Of course, once this was explained to us, several of us saw the logic in doing well in the aptitude areas for pilot while not trying so hard in the others. Like many great ideas, however, it didn't work. We simply could not tell which tests were for pilot and which were for the other jobs. It seemed like all of them were for all of us. We weren't told our scores at that time, so we all kept worrying.

The three weeks finally drew to a close. This is when the stanine scores all came together and we learned our fate. We were marched into the Personnel Office and lined up. One by one we approached the desk and gave our name.

We were told that if the assignment didn't match our preference, we could have one try at an appeal. That didn't really fill me with comfort, for I did not hear of any appeal that changed the test results.

My turn. I approached the desk, came to attention and saluted.

"Peters, Thomas J."

The officer thumbed through his stack of qualification scores.

He looked up at me. "Hmmm," was all he said. That really got my heart pounding—after all, this was the moment that would define the rest of my time in the military.

"Peters, Thomas J., right?"

"Yes, sir."

"Your preference sheet says you want to be a pilot, is that correct?"

"Yes, sir!" I thought the extra emphasis might help. This was making me REALLY nervous, now.

"Well, Peters, you scored a stanine of nine on pilot suitability."

Yee, Haw! I thought. *Flight school here I come!*

"But," He continued, "It's interesting that you scored a seven on Navigator and a six on Bombardier. Those scores qualify you for any of them. It seems you will be successful wherever the Air Force chooses to send you."

My heart dropped to my shoes—or even lower. *Oh, no!*

"Well," he went on, "at the present time, your preference still counts, and nine is very determinative. So…"

He slid a paper across the desk.

"...this is your assignment sheet. If you agree with your assignment, sign at the bottom."

I quickly scanned the paper. Name, serial number, la-de-da-de-da... Ah, there it is, "Training Assignment—PILOT TRAINING." *Yee, Haw, indeed!!* I couldn't sign it fast enough!

I was assigned to the preflight school at—yep, Kelly Field. I just had to move to a different barracks.

IT'S NOT EASY

The move was simple, but temporary. A few days later we packed up again and moved across the creek to the new "San Antonio Cadet Training Center". We also learned that the Preflight course that had been four weeks in duration was now expanded to nine weeks. Something that I quickly found out was that "Preflight Training" was all about "Pre-" and not about "-flight". Classes, classes, classes! When we weren't in class, we were doing physical training. We heard airplanes, and we saw airplanes at a distance, but we didn't go anywhere near one. I didn't really mind any of the classes or physical stuff, but I wanted to FLY! It was turning out that becoming a pilot certainly was NOT "as easy as signing up for an English Lit. class", as the recruiter expressed it.

I was also surprised at the intellectual level of some of my fellow students. Our courses were heavy on math and physics, but at what I thought of as an elementary level. I was shocked at how poorly many of the fellows did in those subjects. I found the classes easy but, of course, I had a degree in Engineering, so math and physics were second nature for me. I quickly found myself acting as tutor for many of the class. The physical stuff didn't strike me as particularly difficult, either. We even had a regular dose of swimming and swimming competitions. I again found myself helping the guys who had never learned to swim. For a couple of weeks, I was even unofficially placed in charge of the swimming activities due to my college experience. So long as I didn't get frustrated about not flying yet, I actually had fun.

During those nine long weeks, two specific things happened to me that I will always remember. The first came during a bull session in the barracks. One of the guys

19

said to me, "Lucky, why does everyone call you 'Lucky'?" By his time, nearly everyone gained a nickname—"Tex" for the guy from Texas, "Cowboy" for the fellow from a cattle ranch. I hadn't picked up on it but, apparently, I had been tagged with the nickname "Lucky". I explained about the recruiter in Stillwater and now it seemed the name had stuck.

One of the other fellows commented, "Lucky, why don't you swear like some of us do?" I thought about that for a moment. "Well, two reasons, I guess. First, on our ranch, the cowboys were a swearing bunch. Some of them couldn't complete a sentence with stringing several swear words together. No offense, but I thought that just sounded ignorant. And then, when any women or children were around, those guys would have to be very careful not to swear in their presence. In fact, some of them didn't even try to clean up their language and simply wouldn't speak at all. That struck me as ridiculous. Second, I think have a sufficient vocabulary to express myself without having to swear."

A third fellow piped in, "You never join in when we're talking about our girlfriends. Why not, don't you like girls?"

That one made me smile. "Guys, your conversations often become descriptions of your conquests. Sure I like girls and I have enjoyed an active dating life, but they are nice girls and I don't want to disrespect them by telling tales." I laughed, "My Momma taught me 'Gentlemen don't kiss and tell'."

I guess after that they thought of me as a "straight arrow" kind of guy. Maybe they were a bit uncomfortable with me, but I never pushed my standards on them and, maybe because they felt they needed me and my help, they continued to be friendly.

It was during the nine weeks of Preflight Training that we began to notice people "washing out", or failing the course. There had been a few who had disappeared from the Classification Course, but now the departures became more obvious. Some of the guys just couldn't manage the academic demands, and others couldn't surmount the physical requirements. One of the biggest causes of failure was the atmospheric tank. Groups of us were placed in a large sealed tank and the atmospheric pressure was continually reduced to simulate the effects of high altitude. Some of the guys couldn't stand the effect on their ears. Others passed out from oxygen starvation at too early a stage. We lost three fellows from our group because of "The Tank". They were reassigned to non-flying duties and transferred out.

Finally, the nine weeks were over. I have to admit that we were becoming much more "military" in our bearing. We had learned much regarding the customs of the service and how to behave like an officer, if we ever really became one. It was taking effect. Finally, we were called together to receive our assignments for Primary Flight Training. Because of the massive expansion of the Army Air Force, the traditional AAF locations for Primary Training had become overwhelmed. As a result, the government decided to contract with civilian flight schools for primary training. The schools would provide the facilities and training and the AAF would provide the airplanes, uniforms, and some essential military oversight.

All of us were extremely eager to start flight training. When we gathered together, a list of 15-20 names were called out and that group was told their destination, followed by another group, and another group. Finally, it was our turn and the eighteen of us in our group were assigned to Arledge Field, near Stamford, Texas for single-engine flight training. We learned that Stamford is very small town located about 40 miles north of Abilene in West Central Texas. Some of the guys groaned that we were being sent to the middle of nowhere, but I didn't care. I wanted to FLY, and they could send me to Podunk Corners for all I cared! The next nine-week period would be spent flying—actually flying, real airplanes! I couldn't start soon enough!

RIDING ON A CLOUD

Our trip on the M-K-T Railroad, which everyone called the "Katy", was long, boring, and uncomfortable. Through what seemed like a miracle, we finally arrived at small station in a small town surrounded by cotton fields. The name "Stamford' was lettered on the end of the weathered depot, so we figured it must be the right place. We disembarked from our rattle-trap coach and were greeted by a grizzled sergeant who lined us up and snarled a welcome. We were expecting a truck to pick us up but, no, we were *marched* out to the airfield. Welcome to Primary Flight Training, Arledge Field and another nine weeks of high-pressured learning!

When we finally got there, we marched through the gate and across an open area surrounded by barracks and other buildings that we came to call the "quad", like several of us had on our college campuses. Then came the thrilling moment; as we passed between the barracks, we came out onto the edge of the flying field and there before us were lines and lines of blue and yellow biplanes marked "U.S. Army." Real airplanes! Airplanes that we would soon be flying! Yee, Haw, indeed!

We were not the only trainees present. Much of the rest of our class was already there and they were ahead of us in getting settled. We went through the usual assignment of barracks, picking a bunk, putting our meager belongings away—in the approved military fashion, of course! And then we started getting acquainted with one another. We realized that we would probably be with some of these fellows all the way into combat, so these new friendships were extra special. Through the rest of that evening and night, three more groups arrived so that, by morning,

23

everyone was present and accounted for. We were members of Arledge Field Class 42-F.

Life got serious at 0700 the next morning.

After breakfast, we were directed to don our new flight suits. We were then mustered by barracks and our names were called off in groups of six. Then each group of six met their flight instructor. Ours was Mr. Homer MacCawley, a fellow who seemed old enough to have flown with the Wright Brothers. But if anyone thought he was just a simple-minded old codger, Mr. MacCawley soon disabused us of the thought.

"Men," he addressed us, "I am going to teach you how to fly. Some of you will learn successfully, some of you will not. All of you will make mistakes; some of you will die by your mistakes. Pay attention to what I teach you and focus on your flying!"

That sure got our attention!

He continued, "How many of you have ever flown in an airplane?"

No one raised his hand.

"O.K., Come with me and we'll take turns going for your orientation ride. You will ride in the rear seat and you will NOT touch any controls! This will be a simple check to let you see what flying feels like."

I was so excited I felt like I could have flown without the airplane!

MacCawley, who soon allowed us to call him "Mac", took us out and gathered us around one of the biplanes.

"Men, this a Model PT-13 primary training airplane built by the Stearman Company in Wichita, Kansas. Technically, Stearman is now a part of Boeing, but everyone still calls this a 'Stearman'. You may think it is an old fashioned airplane because it is a biplane. If you think that, you are wrong. This is the finest primary training aircraft in the world and it can do things that will scare you silly. Respect your airplane, but don't be afraid of it."

Because I was standing closest to him, Mac directed me into the back seat as the first to go. He showed me how to fasten the parachute harness and how to fasten the seat harness.

"O.K., son, what's your name?"

"Peters, sir."

"O.K, Peters, keep your feet on the floor and your hands in your lap!"

Soon, Mac had us following in a long line of other planes heading to the runways. I learned Arledge had four paved runways, so we didn't have long to wait before we could take off. Mac advanced the throttle and we thundered into motion. As the plane accelerated along the runway, I was thrilled by the sensation of speed. It suddenly got quieter and I realized we were flying. I felt like we riding on a cloud. I wasn't queasy or nervous—I was in heaven! The entire sensation of flight was wonderful beyond words. I wished we could've stayed up forever, but after circling the airfield, Mac lined us up and brought us back down. We taxied back to the rest of the group.

Mac climbed out and turned to help me out of the rear cockpit.

"Well, Peters, what do you think?"

My rapturous expression must have answered for me. "Good, you seemed to be enjoying it."

"I loved it, sir! That's the most marvelous thing I've ever done!"

He chuckled. "Well, there's plenty more where that came from!"

I joined the rest of the guys as the next cadet went for his ride. Naturally, everyone wanted me to describe my experience in detail. I just could not find the right words to describe the sensations. Finally, all I could say was, "You'll see for yourself!"

As the morning wore on and each of us got to ride, I was surprised that, despite all the physical testing we'd been through, a couple of the fellows didn't really like the ride. Sam Wilson, whose bunk was two down the line from mine, came back looking visibly green. "I couldn't hold on tight enough!" He exclaimed. "I was sure I'd fall out. The way the plane squished around in the air was awful! I just knew we'd fall right of the sky. I feel sick!" He sure looked it!

Elmer Dowd was the other. He wasn't green like Sam, but he was clearly uncomfortable. "I was sort-of O.K until we turned. When he banked that airplane, I did all I could to straighten it up. I leaned, I pushed, but it just leaned right over anyway. That was awful!"

I guess some guys like the *idea* of flight, but just can't tolerate the *reality* of it. I just knew that I thought the whole experience was marvelous!

By that afternoon, Sam had been taken up again and the result was just as bad, if not worse, than his first try. Late that day, he packed his belongings and was gone. Elmer also got another try and he apparently calmed himself because he did OK that time. He stayed with us.

Our days settled into a routine. One day we had ground school in the morning and flight instruction in the afternoon. The next day was flight in the morning and school in the afternoon. Of course, because there were still five of us sharing Mac's time, our flight time was precious. Mac was strict, but a good teacher.

I can't say the same for the ground school instructor. He insisted on being called *Mister* Baxter, and he made sure we knew he was a *professional* high school teacher who had contracted to teach us. He was arrogant and unpleasant. Worst of all, he was a terrible teacher. It quickly became obvious to us that he had no idea about the aviation topics he was supposed to teach us. We heard through the grapevine that the AAF was starting "instructor schools" for people like him. Unfortunately for all of us, he didn't go off to school while we there. At least, much of the time, he just showed us training films, and they were interesting.

Before each flying session, we would check the schedule board to see what time each of us was scheduled with Mac. When it was time, we would go check out a parachute and some of the smaller guys would also check out a cushion that would scoot them closer to the rudder pedals. Then it was out to the flight line.

Each plane had a "plane captain"—an enlisted mechanic who was responsible for the upkeep of the airplane. Each pilot performed a designated "pre-flight inspection" of the airplane, even though the "captain" had already done a much more thorough look. The inspection was done carefully and precisely. Mac taught me how. The instructor had to sign off on an inspection sheet before each flight, and we learned how to do so also. I loved simply climbing into the cockpit. I would get all buckled in and I would put on the headphones so Mac could talk to me. It wasn't two-way, though. It was actually just a simple speaking tube going from him straight to my ears. I learned how to do all of the cockpit checks, how to start the engine, and how to signal the plane captain to remove the wheel chocks. Just learning how to taxi properly was exciting. Sometimes in more ways than one: for example, if I put the brakes on too hard, the tail would try to come up. Not good! Or if I used too much brake instead of the rudder to turn the plane in the prescribed series of "S"-curves as we taxied, it would suddenly swerve hard. Also not good! Once we got to the runway and checked for other planes coming in, we would take off. At first, Mac would just have me hold the control stick lightly and follow him as he made the maneuvers. But it wasn't long before he let me do them. I was flying!

Learning to fly straight and level was harder than I expected. Maintaining a proper visual reference to the ground was tricky. I'd keep staring at a spot on the horizon and, as we moved toward my spot, my course would wander off. I finally learned how to watch the horizon, not a specific spot, and then all was well. Doing turns, climbs and glides properly also took concentration and practice. My first try at taking off wasn't too bad. Advance the throttle steadily and maintain my path down the runway with the rudder. Stick back slightly. At the right speed, the plane would gently lift off. The only surprise was how much rudder it took to track straight.

I will always remember my first landing. We'd been pretty high off the ground practicing establishing the proper glide angle and I was beginning to feel pretty comfortable at it. Then Mac spoke:

"O.K, Peters, take us back to the field." Oh, boy! I was getting to put all the maneuvers into practice! When we got there, Mac spoke again.

"See if you can line us up with runway 35." I did, more or less.

"Now establish your proper glide angle the way we've been practicing." I concentrated hard and complied.

"Good. Now watch the runway and stay lined up with it. Maintain your glide until we're just above the runway, then ease gently back on the stick and she'll settle right down."

He must have glanced in his mirror and seen the concern etched on my face.

"Relax. You're doing fine."

It happened just as he said. The plane settled right down onto the runway. It wasn't a perfect three-point landing—it was more of a one-point-at-a-time landing, but we were down.

"Good job. Now apply the throttle and take off. We'll go around and do it again."

Which we did—again and again and again. We were required to make 175 landings during the 60 hours flying of our Primary training and Mac would make sure we met the requirement!

Then there came the day when we practiced stalls and spins. I should explain that a "stall" in an airplane is not like a stall in a car. In a car, a "stall" means you killed, or stopped, the engine. In an airplane, a stall is when there is insufficient airflow over the wings to sustain lift. No lift means the plane sinks or falls. Obviously a pilot needs to know how to avoid a stall or, at least, how to manage one. We did power off stalls and power on stalls. That old Stearman was pretty predictable and stall recoveries were logical and rather simple. When it stalled, it would essentially stop flying and it would fall off to the left. Recovery was simple, just point the nose down to gain airspeed and level the wings. The airplane would gain speed, regain lift, and all was well. Once, following one of our recoveries, Mac directed me to again regain our altitude.

He then told me to adjust the trim to a nose-heavy condition. That struck me as strange, but I trusted Mac, so I did as instructed. He then had me pull up slightly into the three-point attitude and reduce throttle, sort of like a power off stall. As we approached the stall, he had me apply full right rudder and keep the stick back. At the point of stall, the airplane suddenly broke over to the right and began to spin downward. The nose of the airplane was pointed straight down and the world was spinning crazily. The earth was coming closer with frightening speed. That's when the thought hit me: *Holy cow! I'm supposed to be FLYING this airplane!*

Mac talked me through it.

"Keep your ailerons neutral."

"Apply full opposite rudder and shove the stick hard forward."

I applied full left rudder and the plane stopped spinning, but we were still diving towards the earth. The hard forward stick magically brought me back into control.

"Ease off on the stick, keep your wings level, and apply power."

The nose started coming up.

"Go ahead and level off."

It worked! But that first spin was the scariest thing that happened to me in Primary Training. We practiced several more spins and I actually came to enjoy spinning. I could even recover after a specified number of spins! Did I say I love flying?

We learned lazy-8's, chandelles, and other general maneuvers. Then we went on to rolls, loops, Immelmann turns, and other acrobatics. And we practiced and practiced.

30

During this time, I experienced that moment all pilots remember forever. We'd been up for about thirty minutes when Mac directed me back to base. I landed us and taxied to the parking ramp, wondering what was wrong. Mac told me to leave the engine running, and he climbed out of the forward cockpit and leaned in to talk to me.

"Not bad, Peters. You know how, so go fly." He jumped down and stood clear of the airplane.

Holy cow! I thought. *I'm going to solo!*

As I taxied out, I kept noticing the empty front cockpit and I realized how much security I placed in having Mac sitting there. Now I was alone. That was my incentive to remember carefully all he had taught me. Boy, was I focused!

It was on my solo flight that I really experienced the *freedom* of flight. I could move in any direction I wanted and I felt truly unfettered. Tuesday, October 6, 1942 will forever remain a day of triumph in my memory.

The flight was simple and successful. A couple of trips around the landing circuit, then land. Success! I would now spend a great deal of my flying time alone, practicing what Mac had taught me.

It was about the time we cadets started soloing that the number of washouts increased. Some of the guys just weren't able to master the basics well enough to solo. If an instructor thought a cadet was not capable, he would report his observations to the Chief Instructor, who would take the cadet up for a check ride. Occasionally, a cadet would manage to hang on, but most didn't. With the washouts, the number of empty bunks increased. And not all were so merciful. Jerry Wilson, from my barracks, had soloed and was up practicing spins. We don't know exactly what happened, but we watched his plane spin down and crash to earth, killing Jerry. Phil Mickelson was lining up for a landing and he banked too sharply at too slow a speed and he stalled in. He lived, but he was in the hospital covered in a full-body cast. It was a sobering lesson to the rest of us that flying could be dangerous.

I haven't mentioned anything about our social life or visits to town. That's because I only went to town once and that was enough. Stamford had about 4000 people when I was there. There were few—if any—people my age. I guess the guys were in the service and the girls were invisible. The single movie show played Hollywood's fairy-tales about the war, and the flying movies were especially laughable, so going to the movies wasn't any fun. The townspeople were nice, but there just wasn't any reason to return to town. It wasn't really a problem, though, because I had plenty of learning-about-flying to do and idle time wasn't an issue.

The nine weeks of Primary sped by. I noticed my skills were getting better and better and I started to feel like the airplane was a part of me. It wasn't like I climbed *into* the plane, it was more like I *put it on.* One day just before our class graduated, Mac had been helping me improve my acrobatics and, as he turned to walk away, he parted by saying; "Peters, you have a nice touch and you fly well. You'll do O.K." Then he walked away. I glowed with pleasure at his praise.

And then it was over. We had completed the nine week primary training course and were ready to advance to Basic. My logbook indicated 61.5 hours of flight and 181 landings. My proficiency scores were all "excellent". Before we left, I made a point of finding Mac and thanking him.

"You're welcome, Peters. Keep up the good work and you'll be a fine fighter pilot. Knock down an enemy for me, OK?"

REFINEMENTS

Another long, slow, dirty train ride brought us all back to the San Antonio area to famous Randolph Field, "The West Point of the Air." The Air Force did not contract out Basic or Advanced training the way they had Primary, so we were back in the land of military behavior and our relaxed days of quasi-civilian life were over. We started the nine weeks of our Basic Flight Training on November 16, 1942. The news from the war was not encouraging with setbacks on all fronts. We had the sense we were needed and we wanted to get "over there" to pitch in. But first, another nine weeks of training, this time in a somewhat larger and more complex airplane, the Vultee "Valiant", or BT-13. We soon learned that everyone referred to the BT-13 as the "Vultee Vibrator" due to the vibrations set up by improper setting of the controllable pitch propeller. It was a low-wing monoplane and it was a bit more complicated than the PT-13. It wasn't intimidating, though, and I found it very easy to fly.

Other than the more complex airplane, training continued as before. We would spend a total of 70 to 75 hours of flying, divided into a "transition phase", involving familiarization with the plane and fundamental operations, and a "diversified phase", which included accuracy in maneuvers and acrobatics, and formation, instrument, navigation, and night flying.

Some items of note: I thought flying a long cross-country assignment was fun, except that I was always just a little concerned that my course-holding might be off and I'd miss my intended destination. I was a little off a couple of times, but I could see my destination "right over there" and correct myself. Another thing was formation flying. I was struck by how much attention it took to stay in proper formation with the planes around me. I just didn't have time to divert my attention to where we were going; I just concentrated on keeping formation. I wondered how the combat pilots could fly a tight formation and still fight. Later, I would find out. I thought night flying was especially peaceful. Droning along on a dark night was relaxing, especially because flying over the wide open spaces of Texas where the widely spaced towns cast welcoming pools of light made course finding relatively simple. Finally, learning to fly on instruments meant lots of time in the Link Trainer, which was located in a building and never left the ground. It was an enclosed box with an instrument panel and controls which the pilot "flew" without outside visual reference. I tried to make a game of it and I seemed to do all right.

Actually, my Basic Flight Training period is sort of a blur. Other than what I just noted, the only big thing that stands out happened right at the end of the course, and that was another sorting out. After the earlier Classification testing, we'd been sorted into training pathways for pilot, navigator, or bombardier. Since then, we pilots had all trained together, that is, until now. At the close of Basic, we were sorted one more time: some pilots to go on with single-engine training for fighters, and some to go to multi-engine training for bombers and cargo flying. The strangest thing was that this important sorting out wasn't based so much on our ability as on our size. That's right, our size.

The reasoning was that fighters are small airplanes with small cockpits whereas bombers are large airplanes with large cockpits. Therefore, fighter pilots should be smaller guys and bomber pilots can be the bigger guys. And that's how we were sorted!

I was actually an "in-between"—I stood 5'11" tall and weighed 160 pounds. I was judged to be on the tall side of the "small" group and I just made it into fighters. Whew!

So my next step was to Advanced Flight Training (Single-Engine), and I was thrilled. I was becoming a proficient pilot who could competently maneuver an airplane and now I would learn the skills necessary to fly a complicated, high-performance aircraft. I was very excited about coming ever-closer to my dream of becoming a fighter pilot. I couldn't wait. I never, in a million years, expected what happened to me in Advanced!

MAYBE NOT SO LUCKY?

We "single-engine guys" were not assigned to Kelly Field as we expected. Kelly was full, so we were sent to a new base named Foster Field, near Victoria, Texas. Another cramped train ride, this time on the Southern Pacific Lines. Arrival at Victoria was just like our other arrivals—orders, marches, and new barracks with bare studs and the tar-paper showing. Fortunately, although we were further east and south, and near the gulf coast, the January temperature was actually a bearable 64 degrees. That was important in those uninsulated new barracks in the winter-time! At least this would be the final nine-week period of our essential flight training before we transitioned into actual fighters. We began our advanced course on Valentine's Day, February 14, 1943.

The initial meeting with my assigned flight instructor was an unpleasant shock. Lieutenant Hobart Sullivan had flown in early combat in the Pacific flying a P-39. Sadly, the P-39 was not a successful fighter and pilot losses were high. Rather than give him vital experience to share with us fledglings, it seemed to twist his mind. He was perpetually angry, easily offended, highly insulting, and impossible to please. I don't know why, but my nickname seemed to especially light his fuse. The trouble started the very first morning.

We were lined up in ranks, expecting to meet our instructors and learn the outline of our training. Instead, Sullivan launched into a profane tirade denigrating us as a bunch of know-nothing , spoiled, college boys. After ranting for ten minutes on how worthless we all were, he stopped for a breath and consulted a paper in his hand.

"Peters, Thomas J." he called out, "front and center!"

Huh? I thought, *What does he want with me?*

I stepped forward as directed. Then he started in:

"I hear you're called 'Lucky', is that right?"

"That's become my nickname, sir," I replied.

"So, you think you're some great flyer—like 'Lucky Lindy Lindbergh' eh? Well, you're NOT a great flyer and I'll prove it the minute I get you up in the air!"

That connection with my nickname certainly never occurred to me, but I was in no position to argue the point.

"Well, Lucky," he ranted, "I see that your qualification scores before coming here are all excellent. That's the last time that'll happen! If I don't wash you out of here in the first two weeks, my name isn't Sullivan. You just think you're some smart college boy who's better than anyone else! Not for long, you're not! I'll show all the rest of you what happens to smart-guys like him!"

I was shocked. We were <u>all</u> shocked. What should have been the most important training we would receive had now become a hell of just trying to survive. This was NOT good!

Later that morning, we reported to the flight line with parachutes in hand, helmets on head, ready to fly. Normally, the instructor would introduce us to our new training airplane. This was especially important because our new trainer was far more powerful and complex than anything we'd ever even ridden in.

When we arrived at the flight line, Sullivan was standing in front of a large, single-engine, two-place trainer with retractable landing gear and who-knew-what-else advanced equipment. I recognized it as an advanced trainer built by North American Aviation named the AT-6 Texan. I only knew that because I'd seen a picture of one.

Sullivan searched the group until he spotted me. "You! Lucky-boy! Get in the front seat!"

This had to be some sort of a bad joke. No orientation to the airplane's features and capabilities, no orientation flight, nothing! Just "Get in the front seat!" It became apparent that I'd need all my so-called luck not only to NOT wash out in the first two weeks, but to NOT get killed in the first two weeks!

In the Army, you do what you're ordered, so I put on my parachute and figured out how to climb into the front seat. Sullivan climbed into the instructor's cockpit behind me. We put on our headphones which, unlike the earlier trainers, really were a two-way radio.

My 'phones came to life. "Hurry up and scan the preflight card and get this airplane started!"

The preflight "card" was a full two pages of detailed instructions of appropriate settings and switch positions necessary before starting the huge 600 horsepower radial engine. I had barely started reading when Sullivan's voice snarled in my ears.

"Come on, smart-boy, get the engine started!"

I tried to ignore him and kept working my way through the instructions. Suddenly, the propeller began to turn and the engine started! Obviously, Sullivan wouldn't wait for me.

"That's the first black mark against you—ignoring your instructor! You won't last long smart-boy! Taxi out to the runway!"

I looked at the control tower and saw we were directed to runway 30. I noticed the wind was light, so I didn't have to worry about a crosswind or anything--that was good.

We got to the runway and got a green light from the tower. I found a lever marked "flaps", so I lowered the flaps. I had no idea how much flap was called for, so I just lowered them all the way. I guessed at the proper settings for the propeller and fuel mixture and advanced the throttle. I immediately learned that the ground handling characteristics of the AT-6 were infinitely more difficult that anything I'd flown so far. I swerved a little, but kept on the runway and we soon lifted off.

"Make a left turn and head out to the practice area."

I had no idea where the practice area was, but I supposed he'd tell me when we got there. After we cleared the end of the runway, I retracted the landing gear and flaps and I was surprised by the airplane's reaction—it sort of mushed when the flaps came up. But then it speeded up and things settled down a bit. I was still at full throttle while climbing out, and I didn't know what to do about the RPMs or manifold pressure, so I just left everything alone. *Maybe he'll tell me what to do...*, I hoped. Instead, he said:

"Well, so far, smart-boy, you've done everything wrong. I'll have you washed out by tonight!" Then he chuckled.

As we approached an area of empty farm fields below, he told me to climb to 6000 feet. When we reached that altitude, he told me to pull the nose up sharply. I did as I was told, but I expected that would lead to either a power-on stall or break into a spin. I had no idea how the AT-6 reacted in either case, so I was tensely trying to be ready for anything. It kept climbing for a surprisingly long time, the result, I am sure, of the huge powerful engine. But all good things come to an end...

Just before we stalled, his voice snarled through the headphones, "Pull the stick full back and kick hard right rudder!"

*O.K.,*I thought, *we'll spin. I suppose all airplanes are brought out of a spin the same way, so that's what I'll do.* Sure enough, we broke into a right-hand spin. I let it turn one complete circle, then I kicked hard left rudder and shoved the stick forward. It worked! We came out of the spin and I was able to gently bring the plane back into level flight. Whew!

"What are you doing, smart-boy? I didn't tell you to come out of the spin yet! Boy, you're making this too easy for me! Take us back to field!"

As I turned us back toward the airfield, he retarded the throttle and adjusted the propeller and mixture. I entered the landing pattern and I guessed when to lower the flaps and landing gear. I also guessed at what our approach speed should be by noting the colored arcs on the airspeed indicator. While I was turning us from our base leg to our final approach leg, he growled again: "Bank steeper!"

That was alarming! I knew if we banked too steeply at too slow a speed, we'd stall and crash. I maintained my current degree of bank.

"I said bank steeper!"

Enough is enough! He may want to die, but I don't! It's time I speak up—besides, he's going to wash me out anyway.

"Sir, if I bank more steeply, we'll stall!"

His response was shocking! "Ha! Gotcha, smart-boy! You just refused a direct order from a superior officer! When we land, you go the barracks and pack your stuff while I report you to the Colonel. You're not so smart after all!"

He landed the plane and taxied us back to the parking ramp. After he shut the engine down and the propeller stopped turning, I climbed out of the cockpit.

"You go wait in the barracks until the Colonel calls for you. Pack your stuff, smart-boy, you're a goner! 'Lucky' my foot!"

* * * * * * * * * *

Upon returning from enjoying his lunch at the diminutive officer's club on base, Colonel Robert Carlson summoned his aide, Lieutenant-Colonel Sidney Watts.

"Sid, bring me the file on a cadet named Peters, Thomas J. Sullivan just gave me a terrible report on this kid; I wonder how he ever passed Primary, let alone made it here."

"Pretty bad, eh?"

"Yeah. According to Sullivan, this Peters has a bad attitude and can't fly to boot."

Fifteen minutes later, the file still hadn't appeared. Colonel Carlson picked up his phone.

"Sid, where's that file?"

"I'm looking, sir, but I can't find it. I'll bring it in as soon as I locate it."

"That's strange. Well, send for Peters to report to me."

"Yes, Sir!"

I had been sitting in the barracks stewing over what had happened and trying to figure out if there was anything I could do about it. As the morning wore on, the other cadets were apparently out flying, and I wondered if Sullivan treated them the way he did me. At lunch time, the other guys came bustling into the barracks speaking in excited tones. It turns out that Sullivan was rough on them, too. They went off to lunch jabbering about the morning, but I had to wait for the Colonel's summons. Finally, an Airman poked his head into the barracks and told me to report to the Colonel right away.

Well, maybe I'll get a chance to explain. Or maybe I'll just be sent packing. This should be interesting!

When I reported, I was kept standing at attention in front of the Colonel's desk as he began to question me.

"Peters, did you refuse a direct order issued by Lieutenant Sullivan?"

"Sir, if you are referring to his order to bank more steeply on approach, yes, sir, I guess I refused his order."

"You guess!" the Colonel said sharply. "What do you mean 'you guess'? What did he order you to do?"

I explained about our landing approach and Sullivan telling me to bank more steeply.

The Colonel paused thoughtfully. "Were you not approaching properly?"

"Sir, my approach was exactly right to reach the runway. I was afraid that if I banked more steeply, we'd stall and crash"

"Did you explain that to Lieutenant Sullivan?

"Yes, sir."

"What did Lieutenant Sullivan say to you?"

I hesitated, but I decided this was my chance to help my own cause. "Sir, Lieutenant Sullivan laughed and said 'Ha! Gotcha, smart-boy!' He then stated he would wash me out for failing to follow an order."

"What!? He said that?"

"Yes, sir."

"Hmmm." The Colonel paused thoughtfully. "Sullivan also states you failed to follow proper procedure in starting the airplane and in establishing the proper conditions for flight. Is that true?"

"I suppose so, sir."

"You suppose!? Did you follow the procedures you have been trained for flying the AT-6 aircraft or didn't you?"

"I don't know, sir."

Now the Colonel was REALLY upset. "You don't know!?" He was nearly shouting. "What do you mean 'you don't know'?!"

At this moment, Lieutenant-Colonel Watts stepped forward. Apparently he had slipped into the office sometime earlier. "Sorry, sir, but here is Peter's file."

The Colonel took the file, but didn't look at it.

"Peters, have you been trained in flying the AT-6 airplane?"

"No, sir."

The Colonel looked stunned. "Then..." But Watts interrupted him. "Sir, I couldn't find the file in the training classes already underway but I did find it among those for the men who reported last night to start training today."

The Colonel was speechless. Finally:

"Peters, when did you report to this base?"

"Last night, sir."

"Then what were you doing flying around in an AT-6 this morning with no training?"

"Sir, I was ordered to by Lieutenant Sullivan."

Carlson looked sharply at Watts. "Sid, you'd better stick around so we both hear this."

"O.K., Peters, start at the beginning and tell us exactly what happened this morning. Tell us everything!"

I did. When I finished, the Colonel asked me a surprising question.

"Peters, what is your impression of Lieutenant Sullivan?"

Oh, boy! This is touchy, but I'll answer honestly.

"Sir, from his comments, Lieutenant Sullivan seems to have it in for college-trained cadets. He railed at all of us about being 'too smart for own good.' It also strikes me that his combat experience has affected his mind."

The Colonel glared at me. "What was your major in school?"

"Engineering, sir."

"Not Psychology?"

I couldn't help but smile. "No, Sir. I'm sorry if I spoke out of turn, Sir."

Colonel Carlson directed me to return to the barracks, but then continued by asking if I'd had any lunch.

"No, Sir. I have not had lunch."

"O.K., Peters, go get some lunch and report back here at 1400."

I saluted, turned, and left the office.

After I had gone, Carlson looked at Watts.

"What do you think, Sid?"

"Well, sir, I believe the kid. I've been hearing some increasingly disturbing rumors about Sullivan. If this story is true, I think he's gone over the edge."

"Let's call three other cadets from Peters' class in here and see what they have to say."

*   *   *   *   *   *   *

I can't say that I enjoyed my lunch, in fact, I THINK I had a hamburger, but I can't say for sure. My insides were churning with worry and frustration over what had happened.

What did I do to deserve this? I've done well all the way the through and suddenly I'm about be sent off to the infantry or something. At least I got to explain, but I don't know if they believe me. This isn't fair! But, since when is life fair? Especially in the Army!

I reported back to the Colonel's office a few minutes before 1400 and was kept waiting in his outer office. Finally, I heard him call me in.

"Peters, we've checked into what you told us earlier and we have confirmed your story. You may return to the barracks and unpack your belongings; you'll be starting your formal advanced flight training tomorrow morning. And, Peters, I understand your nickname is 'Lucky'—well you sure earned that name this morning! You're fantastically lucky you didn't kill yourself up there!"

Whew!

The next morning, we were again ordered to the flight line, dressed in flying gear. I dreaded seeing Sullivan because I could imagine how angry he'd be at me, probably thinking I lodged a complaint about him.

Instead, we were greeted by a stranger. "Men, I am Captain James Stafford, and I have been assigned as your flight instructor." Nothing was said about Sullivan, although we later heard a rumor that he had been transferred out. Captain Stafford continued: "I am not usually one of the pilots who begin your AT-6 transition; I usually take over for the last part of your training to teach you combat maneuvers and gunnery. But I'm here now and I'll stay with you the rest of the way through."

In talking later, we all agreed that Stafford seemed like a good guy who would try to teach us well. And so it was.

The AT-6 was a lot of airplane, very large and complex and it required constant attention to fly it properly. In that regard, it was the ideal advanced trainer and it earned its nickname of "The Baby Fighter". So far, through my entire air force "career", I had found the training demanding, but I had enjoyed every minute of it. It now became even more demanding because the airplane was far more complex. We spent a lot of time practicing tight formation flying, we also learned all of the conventional combat maneuvers, and we practiced, practiced, practiced. But I was having a ball!

One afternoon, I found myself sitting with Captain Stafford in the cafeteria and I used the opportunity to thank him for working so hard to teach us properly. He had turned out to be a stickler for correctness and would not ignore any sloppy flying, but he put his full effort into training us right. His answer to my comment was revealing: "Well, Peters, I look at it this way—when I go back into combat, I might be flying with one of you guys and I want to be sure you know what you're doing!" Seemed like a good philosophy to me!

As we progressed in our skills, we were granted more leeway in our practice time. At this time, a couple of the guys did something really stupid. They were up practicing close formation flying when one of them suggested it would be fun to drop down and "buzz" the farm where his new girlfriend lived. A bad idea, but off they went. Now, I admit it really is exciting to fly low at 200 miles per hour— but...

My classmates proceeded to really mow the grass at the farm but, unbeknownst to them, the county sheriff was visiting the girlfriend's dad. His visit had nothing to do with us but, since the base had opened, he was receiving an increasing number of complaints from the civilians about "low-flying aircraft" and the sheriff was getting tired of the complaints. My pals were so low and close it was easy to read the aircraft numbers painted on the sides of the fuselage. When they finished having their fun and landed back at Foster Field, they were greeted by a jeep with big letters "MP" painted on them. The pilots were "escorted" to the Colonel's office and we were later told his tirade could have blistered the paint from the walls. He decided to make an example of the two cadets, so the entire class was called to formation with the two of them standing conspicuously front and center. Colonel Carlson described to all of us what they had done and why that was wrong behavior, and he then announced that, rather wash them out, he would have mercy on them. Both of the fellows relaxed a bit until they heard their sentence—they were restricted to base until our class graduated and they were held back to finish their course with the class behind us. That was really painful because all of us had become close friends and we didn't want to be separated. Oh, well, it was certainly better than being washed out. The rest of us became much more careful. The low-level stuff abated somewhat, but we were careful to do it where we knew there were no people in the area. I imagine, however, that milk production from the local cows' declined precipitously!

When we were well into the advanced program, the top students were selected to begin gunnery training. We would get a preliminary 20 hours of training in those advanced trainers that had a pair of .30 caliber guns in the wings, and then we would go forward to get an additional 10 hours in an actual fighter. This was REALLY getting to be fun!

My admiration of Captain Stafford grew even greater at this time. He led a flight of several of us out to Matagorda Island to the new gunnery range. He had us circle and watch while he described how to approach and fire on a stationary target. Then he demonstrated. Wow! He blew the targets to bits! I doubt even one of his shells missed and we were very impressed. Our initial efforts were not so impressive. I was surprised how the slightest change in stick or rudder had a huge effect on the stream of bullets. My stream of gunfire was all over the place and it was mesmerizing how the smallest pressure on the rudder pedals caused the shell strikes to weave and even circle. I remember thinking, *This is going to take a lot of practice!*

But, as the tired old saying goes, "practice makes perfect" and, although we certainly didn't achieve perfection, we did improve greatly and soon we were able to score sufficiently well to continue advancing our training. And then came a very big day. Captain Stafford took us out to a different part of the flight line and there before us were real fighters! There were a half-dozen early-model P-40s— real fighters with real guns—and we would get to fly them! First, of course, we had to study the pilot's manual and practice cockpit orientation—blind-folded, naturally. But came the day when I found myself ready to fly the first single-seat fighter I had ever been in. Prior to then, all my flying experience was in dual-cockpit trainers. Even though I'd been flying alone more and more often, it was still rather intimidating to actually be in there alone, with no place for an instructor to assist me. Scary, but exciting.

My first surprise was that the P-40 was, in some ways, easier to fly than the AT-6—especially its ground handling. The P-40 was also the first airplane I had flown with an inline engine rather than a radial engine, which certainly helped forward visibility. We had started our gunnery training by firing at stationary targets on the ground and, as we improved, advanced to shooting at towed targets in the air. Some of the guys had a little trouble learning to lead a moving target—called "deflection" shooting but, on our ranch, I had learned how to lead a target when I was just a boy shooting at fast-moving jack rabbits. Now, in the P-40, things happened much faster because the fighter was much faster. It was a fun challenge to hit the towed target and I was having the time of my life.

And then, suddenly, it was all over. Our initial training was over—we made it through all of the early classification and pre-flight screenings, we made it through Primary, Basic, and now Advanced flight training, and the day was now at hand when we would graduate and receive two important things: our pilot's wings and our officer's bars. We would officially become officers and pilots! But, before the fun and formalities, we had one other vitally important event: we received our assignments for actual fighter training.

We gathered in the barracks and Lieutenant-Colonel Watts started reading off names and assignments and our excitement was palpable. Some of the guys were sent to combat training in the P-40. Some were sent to fly the P-39. To groans of disappointment, some guys were sent to non-combat flying assignments. My group was thrilled—there were ten of us called off, and we realized we were the top ten graduates of the class—we were assigned to Farmingdale, Long Island, New York for combat training in the P-47 Thunderbolt. The P-47 was the hottest thing in the air and we felt privileged to be assigned to fly them. Can I say it again? Yee, Haw, indeed!!

One fun task before graduation was the acquiring of our actual officer's uniforms. We had been wearing a Flight Cadet uniform that was neither officer nor enlisted—we were sort of in-between. So we went to a warehouse on base and were issued our complete set of officer's and pilot's uniforms. This time, some care was taken to be sure everything fit properly. We weren't allowed to wear them until graduation day, though.

After we hauled it all back to the barracks, one of the guys said he heard that there was a lady in town who would custom fit the dress uniform pieces for a reasonable price. Her name was Mrs. Alanby and I'm sure she expected us. I was a bit skeptical about a little old lady in Victoria, Texas being able to properly alter our official AAF uniforms, but she did. In fact, she did a marvelous job and she became something of a legend in our corner of the AAF.

One evening just before graduation, during a general bull session in the barracks, Lieutenant-Colonel Watts dropped by and joined in. He shared some interesting information with us. He told us that recent reports had indicated that nearly forty percent of aviation cadets had failed to complete the course of flight training. The number of washouts was highest in primary and lowest in advanced, which did not surprise us. He also told us that the students eliminated from pilot training were not lost to the AAF, since most of them were reassigned to other types of instruction or service. The majority of those who had the qualifications were sent to bombardier or navigator schools. If not so qualified, they were assigned to other combat-crew positions, which normally required courses in flexible gunnery and one of the various companion specialties, such as airplane mechanics. We found his comments to be a fascinating look at the inside operation of the AAF.

Graduation day, April 28, 1943, was a blur. We all arose and scrubbed and shaved until we shined. On with our spiffy new uniforms and ready for formation at 0930. We formed up and marched over to the big parade ground, but rather than go right out onto the grounds, we were placed "at ease" and we milled around at the edge of the grassy field. A bleacher had been erected and we were all surprised at the large crowd that overflowed the bleachers. In front of the bleachers was a reviewing stand were Colonel Carlson and other VIPs would be seated.

At a few minutes before ten o'clock, the base band arrived and we graduates reformed our companies and fell in behind the band. We were cautioned that, if we had ever looked sharp, it had better be today. Not just because it was graduation, but because General Hap Arnold, the head of the entire United States Army Air Forces, was on the reviewing stand! Apparently, he had come home from Europe for treatment of some health issues and he stopped by Foster Field to take part in our graduation. What an honor!

At ten o'clock sharp, the band started playing a Sousa march, commands were barked, and we were on our way. The actual pass-in-review struck me as similar to a landing approach; we started off downwind, turned left onto base leg, and then left again onto final. Now it was our turn to pass the reviewing stand and we really did look sharp— probably the best marching we ever did. As we approached the reviewing stand, from the corner of my eye I could see a General Officer on the stand, sort of stocky and a bit rumpled looking. We got the command "eyes right!" and we snapped our heads to the right. The high-ranking officers all saluted us and that felt good. Just as we passed the stand, a roar came from overhead and scores of AT-6's in perfect formation flew overhead. It was like rolling thunder and the ground shook. I was so touched I was speechless.

After we passed in review, we lined up in two ranks facing the stand and the officers came along the line to present us with our "hardware". When they reached me, Colonel Carlson called my name: "Peters, Thomas J.!" I stepped forward and General Arnold himself shook my hand and handed me my wings and the single gold bar of a Second

Lieutenant. Wow, was I ever thrilled! As they passed to the next cadet, Colonel Carlson leaned in towards me and whispered "Good job, Lucky! Keep it up!" I was too stunned to even smile.

My parents had come down from Oklahoma to watch me graduate and my Dad was so proud I thought he'd bust. Mom was too, but she was also being "Mom": "Son, have they been feeding you enough? Are you feeling well? You certainly look trim! I like your uniform. Don't you have any medals like those older men?" I couldn't keep up with her rapid-fire questions, so I just hugged her.

FARMINGDALE

So far, I haven't said much about my friends, the other pilots. At this point, it is appropriate to introduce them, because we'd all been in it together and they will show up throughout the rest of the story. In alphabetical order, they are:

Roger Adams, Springfield, Missouri ("Rog" {sounds like "rahj"})

Phil Briscoe, Cleveland, Ohio ("Phil" {What else would it be?})

Peter Davis, Lawrence, Kansas (Since I was "Lucky", he got called "Pete")

Elmer Franklin, Kansas City, Missouri ("E". {It was easier than the entire 'Elmer'})

Lewis Grantham, Little Rock, Arkansas ("Reb". {In fact, his 'southern' accent was so strong, it took a while to be able to really understand what he was saying!})

Alan Hawkins, Marshalltown, Iowa. ("Alan". {He was a very formal kind of guy and wanted everyone to use his full regular name.})

Wilfred Jamison, Fort Worth, Texas ("Rustler". Occasionally "Will". {Fort Worth claimed to be "Where the west begins", so the cowboy reference was fitting.})

Benjamin Johnson, Wichita, Kansas. ("P.K". {His father was a preacher, so he was a 'Preacher's Kid'})

Robert Washburn, Hosmer, South Dakota. ("Bobby". {Nothing else seemed to fit.})

53

So there they are. We called ourselves the "Top 10" because of our standing at the end of advanced school. Yes, I suppose that was a bit presumptuous, but we were proud of having done so well, and we were proud of having been selected to fly the incredible P-47.

With the excitement of graduation behind us, we headed for Long Island. We again boarded a train and began a long, circuitous trip that seemed to take us all over creation. At least we had plenty of time to catch up on our sleep. After four days, we finally found ourselves at the Republic Airport in Farmingdale, adjacent to the Republic Aircraft factory that produced the P-47. We weren't the first group there, for the 63rd fighter squadron of the 56th fighter group was already there getting their new fighters.

We arrived on May 6, 1943, and we settled in and met the officers in charge of our fighter transition training. We also learned that we were not joining the 63rd, nor were we forming a new squadron, but we would become replacement pilots for units in combat. At this point, my log book indicated a total of 236.5 hours of flight time. It seemed like a lot—until I met the P-47.

The P-47 was breathtaking. It is huge and heavy, weighing over twelve thousand pounds. A six-ton fighter didn't seem to make sense, but it was a big, beautiful, high-performance airplane. We learned it was nicknamed the "jug", allegedly because if you visualized it standing on its nose, it was shaped a huge milk jug. (We also later learned it could stand for the appropriately descriptive word "juggernaut".) As we first walked around one, the cockpit seemed so high in the air you could get a nosebleed just sitting in it. Rustler summed up our feelings: "This looks like an airplane that can take punishment and still bring you home. I like that!"

Starting the following Monday, we were issued a pilot's manual and told to study it carefully. Through that week, we also watched a series of training films about flying the P-47. One I especially enjoyed started off in a way totally unlike any training film I had ever seen. The opening scenes featured comedian Lew Lehr and a beautiful girl portraying a golfer. Her form was outstanding—as a golfer and otherwise! It did eventually get around to the P-47.

We also enjoyed a fascinating lecture one afternoon. We learned that the United States and Britain had agreed on a "Germany first" priority in conducting the war, and that the U.S. Navy wasn't too happy about that. We learned that that our Army Air Force was devoted to a daylight precision-bombing approach, as opposed to the British, who had sustained excessive losses in daytime bombing and shifted to area bombing at night. It was explained that our precision bombing plan was unproven and the British were very skeptical of our chances for success. The initial elements of our Eighth Air Force were in England, attempting to prove the validity of our plan, and they had enjoyed enough success that precision attacks seemed feasible. One essential belief in American plans was the axiom carried over from the First World War that "the bombers will always get through." Our B-17 and B-24 heavy bombers were very heavily armed—in fact, the B-17 was called the "Flying Fortress"—and the theory was that by having a large enough force of heavily armed bombers flying in a carefully planned formation, the bombers would be able to protect themselves. Early experience in Europe, however, was beginning to show some flaws in that thinking, and that was where we came in. The increasing awareness that the bombers experienced much lower losses when they were provided fighter protection led to a growing desire for a high altitude fighter-interceptor that could fly and fight at the high altitudes the bombers needed. The P-47 was the fighter to meet that need. We appreciated being "in-the-know" and it helped us understand our role as we trained for combat.

We spent the first week studying the manuals and watching the films. We watched the movies over and over (especially the one with the golfer-girl!), and we began quizzing each other on the details from the stuff we studied. I was struck by how much it was like our impromptu study groups in college. We then started to inspect an actual P-47, being shown inside the various access hatches and under the huge engine cowling. We spent a lot of time learning where the engine turbocharger was located and how it worked. We were required to draw a diagram of its various inputs and outputs and explain how it functioned. (In brief, the turbocharger took in exhaust air from the engine and ran it through a sort of compressor that then fed the higher pressure air into the engine air intake. It served to boost the intake air pressure as the plane went higher in altitude where the outside air was "thinner". It gave the massive engine much greater power at high altitudes which is very important for flying and fighting at the high altitudes where the bombers flew!)

We then climbed into the cockpit for familiarization. My first thoughts regarding the P-47 cockpit were: 1. It's really high up above the ground, 2. Although it was crammed with dials, levers and switches, it was actually rather roomy, and 3. The pilot's seat was the most comfortable I had ever sat in. P.K. described it as being "like a lounge chair", and I certainly agreed. We spent several days memorizing the location of all the aforementioned dials, switches, and levers followed by numerous practice sessions blindfolded to test our familiarization.

After that, we concentrated on the procedures to set the airplane up for flight and to how to get the engine started.

We were quizzed over and over again about the minutest details:

"Where do you start your 'clockwise check'?" (Left side, gas selector on "Main".)

"What are the proper settings for the oil and intercooler shutters?" (Both open.)

"How far do you crack the throttle?" (1/2 to ¾ inch.)

"What setting for prop level and mixture control?" (Prop set full forward and mixture in idle cutoff.)

"Cowl flaps?" (Open.)

And so on, and so on! These are just a few of the settings before even starting the engine!

During the third week, we were finally ready to try to fly. Well, maybe "try" isn't quite the right word—after all—we would either fly or...

On that fateful morning, the transition instructor pilot stood on the right wing root and leaned into the cockpit. He had me state everything I was doing and made sure I didn't miss anything. After starting the engine, I was allowed to taxi out, take off, and fly in the vicinity of the airfield while I got the feel of the plane. It was pure ecstasy. That huge fighter handled superbly, responsive, yet stable. It flew fast—very fast! Talk about an aerial hot rod! The Thunderbolt would dive like a rock and we had been impressed not to let it get away from us too close to the ground. My only disappointment was that it seemed sluggish in a climb, which was puzzling considering the huge 2000 horsepower engine.

We began our formal fighter transition training by starting with learning the Thunderbolt's response in stalls and spins, and then moving on to learn an ever-increasing repertoire of combat maneuvers.

An evening bull session:

Rustler: "If I'm going to have someone shooting at me, I'd sure rather be in P-47 than anything else!"

Bobby: "Yeah, brother! Imagine the difference between this and those P-40s we flew for gunnery—they were like tin cans by comparison!"

Alan: "I think I prefer the air-cooled radial engine to the liquid-cooled inline types. It seems much more rugged."

Reb: "You-all oughta head over to Republic and get jobs as salesmen!"

We laughed, but it was unanimous that we loved the P-47 and we looked forward to entering combat with a big ol' "Jug" wrapped around us!

That's why it was such a shock for all ten of us to be summoned to the commander's office one afternoon a few days later after flying all morning.

SHOCK!!

We were still in our flight gear when we reported as ordered. We were ushered into the office and were told to remain at ease and come close to the desk. Then the bottom dropped out of our world.

"Men," Lieutenant-Colonel Wellesley, head of our training group, began, "there has been a change of plans—a rather dramatic change of plans."

We looked at each other in confusion.

He continued: "The bombing offensive based in England has progressed nicely, but we have learned some crucial facts. Not only do we now realize that the bombers need fighter escort in order to prevent unacceptable bomber losses, we also now know that the depth of penetration into enemy airspace is limited by the effective range of the fighter escort. So far, most of the escort has been provided by British Spitfires and our P-38s and P-47s, none of which can reach very deeply into Germany. They cannot help the bombers on missions deeper into enemy territory. What we need is a truly long-range fighter escort."

We were hanging on his every word.

"We are having limited success by adding external fuel tanks, especially to the P-47. The fighters use the gas in the external tanks first, then drop them and fly and fight on the internal fuel. That's why we call them "drop tanks", but they haven't really solved the problem and they still can't go far enough. Fortunately, there is just coming into production a fighter that has, so far, proven to be exactly the solution we need."

The deeply questioning look on our faces must have been palpable.

"That airplane is the P-51 Mustang."

We were shocked. Elmer blurted out "But the P-51 is just a dressed-up P-40. It's a dog!"

Wellesley looked sharply at Elmer. Reb couldn't keep quiet, either: "Sir, everyone knows that what Elmer says is true. The P-51 uses the same Allison engine as the P-40. It can't fly high and it can't fly fast. Like he says, it's a dog!" The rest of us nodded in strong agreement.

Wellesley took a deep breath and refrained from dressing us down. He explained: "Men, I know that was the reputation of the P-51. Our air force wasn't really even interested in it and only bought a few. The British have used them as ground attack planes with good success and their pilots offer strong praise for their handling characteristics but, you are correct, those early Mustangs didn't fly high or fast and certainly weren't suitable for long range, high altitude escort. But surprising things have happened while you have been in training."

You could have cut our skepticism with a knife.

"An enterprising English pilot, a test pilot in fact, was aware of the limitations of the Mustang, but he noted the general similarity of the shape of the Mustang nose with that of the Spitfire. You might know that the Spitfire is powered by a Rolls Royce engine called the 'Merlin' that is powerful and features a two-stage supercharger for high altitude performance. This English fellow wondered what would happen if you put a Merlin engine in a Mustang. To make a long story short, they tried it and result was astounding. The Allison-powered P-51 topped out about 12-15,000 feet with a top speed of about 340 miles per hour. With the Merlin engine, it suddenly reached 42,000 feet and a top speed of 440 miles per hour, one hundred miles per hour faster and nearly three times the altitude! In addition, the Mustang already has a large on-board fuel capacity that gives it a range on internal fuel that is greater than a P-47 with added external tanks. Further tests in England and here in the US confirmed this amazing transformation. In addition, the higher speed showed another of the Mustang's wonders, the special laminar-flow wing cross-section not only reduced the plane's drag but also allowed it remarkable handling. The Merlin-powered P-51 is as near to a 'wonder plane' as I have ever heard. Therefore, we are removing you men from P-47 training and reassigning you new P-51 training. You will be among the first to become a P-51 long-range escort squadron."

We were shocked and wouldn't give in easily.

My turn to comment: "Sir, I appreciate what you've told us, but we are so far into our P-47 program that I'm wondering if it might not be more effective for us to continue and a class behind us who are not so advanced be reassigned?"

He paused and again drew a deep breath. "Men, you obviously do not understand what you've been told. First, although the P-47 is a fine airplane, you are going to be among the lucky pilots who will fly a very high performance airplane that is critically needed and one that will assure the success of our efforts to defeat a formidable foe. You also don't understand that your orders are already cut and there will be no further discussion!"

That, as they say, was that.

We were told (ordered) to return to the barracks, get into our regular uniforms, and pack our belongings for immediate transfer. Much to our surprise, "immediate" really meant "immediate". We hadn't been packing for more than a few minutes when an enlisted man came in and hustled us outside where there was a truck awaiting us. We anticipated—or maybe "dreaded" is a better word—another long train ride and we assumed this was our ride to the station. Wrong! In yet another shocking surprise in a morning filled with shocking surprises, the truck simply took us out to the flight line where we found a C-47 transport waiting--rather impatiently, it seemed-- for us to get aboard. Pete's comment was appropriate: "Wow! They sure want to get rid of us!" I was wondering if, rather, they really wanted to get us to where we were going in hurry. Hmmm...

After we strapped into our seats, we had the first opportunity to look at our orders and see where we were going—Luke Field, near Phoenix, Arizona. Arizona??!!

SAGEBRUSH, SAND, AND SUN

Afterward, we weren't sure if the airplane ride was really any improvement over a long train ride. The seats on the transport were just canvas webbing and the interior was noisy and uncomfortable. We did eventually arrive at Luke Field and noted the sign above the operations building : "37th Flying Training Wing", and we especially enjoyed the one just beneath it: "Home of the Fighter Pilot". To ten dirty and tired would-be fighter pilots, that sounded really good.

The next morning, the surprises continued. We gathered in a large classroom and met the other fifteen men we'd be training with. After a few minutes, a Lieutenant-Colonel came in started speaking.

"Men, you are here to transition to flying and fighting in an amazing fighter aircraft. I am convinced that the P-51 Mustang is destined to become the finest fighter in the world, and you will be among the pioneers to take it into battle." Elmer and I glanced at each other skeptically. "We also have," he continued, "an unusual situation wherein about half of you have already been deeply involved in training on P-47s. You will find that the two airplanes are vastly different from one another but, your recent training allows us to somewhat accelerate your transition here. We'll work you hard and you are expected to devote yourself to successfully meeting our stringent requirements."

Accelerated? Stringent requirements? I couldn't help but be a bit concerned and thought to myself, *This is going to be challenging. I hope I'm up to it!*

Our speaker went on: "You are training together to become the 501st fighter squadron of the 336th Fighter Group in England. And now I am pleased to introduce your squadron commander, Major James Stafford."

James Stafford? 'Major' James Stafford? Can it really be him?

Into the room walked the familiar figure of the former Captain, and now Major, James Stafford. Yes, our instructor from back in advance flight training! We ten looked at each other with surprised glee. Reb couldn't contain himself: "Yes, Suh!!" He exclaimed in that southern drawl. He then started clapping and so did the rest of who know and like Major Stafford. The other fellows wondered what in the world was going on. After all, in the military, you do NOT applaud your commanding officer like some famous singer or something!

Stafford smiled, especially at us.

"Well, men, as you can tell, I am acquainted with some of these hoodlums from an earlier time."

We howled. "Hoodlums?! We were your best students!" Now we were all laughing so hard we could barely breathe. The Lieutenant-Colonel was totally bewildered.

"O.K.," Major Stafford said, still smiling, "let's get serious now." He then explained to the rest of the group about our time together during advanced training.

Oh, boy! I thought, *This couldn't be any better! We'll really learn how to fly the P-51, that's for sure! Hooray!*

Our familiarization with the P-51 began right then, and continued hot and heavy thereafter. A fighter pilot spends a great deal of time on what might be termed "engine management"—the various engine settings and limits appropriate for our various maneuvers and aircraft attitudes. We had just spent a lot of time learning the management of the air-cooled Pratt and Whitney R-2800 radial engine. Now we had to relearn everything on a totally different liquid-cooled inline engine and we were now drawing diagrams of the cooling system in addition to other systems new to us. The engine that changed the P-51 from an O.K low-level airplane into an exceptional high-altitude airplane was the British Rolls-Royce "Merlin" engine. It is a V-12 power plant and incorporates a built-in two-stage supercharger. Because North American Aviation was building the re-engined Mustangs as fast as they could, Rolls Royce couldn't manage to build all the engines the British needed and all we needed, too. Therefore, contracts had been given to the Packard Motorcar Company to build Merlins here in America. In fact, North American was not only building Mustangs at their Southern California plant, but they had also opened a new factory near Dallas, Texas as well.

Study, study, study! Quiz, quiz, quiz! We crammed into ten days what would normally have taken two weeks or more. We walked around the sleek fighters, examining every nook and cranny (What IS a "nook" and "cranny" anyway?). We started our cockpit familiarization right away. As we were accelerating our training, Major Stafford encouraged us to assist our fellow students so they could keep up. Did I mention we were very busy?

One afternoon, I was walking out with Alan, Pete, and Phil to practice again in the cockpit when we heard the unmistakable sound of three Mustangs passing overhead. (I always thought a taxiing Mustang sounded about like a big tractor, but in the air, that Merlin sings a beautiful song!) We watched as the three pilots flew over in perfect formation, then lined up and landed in perfect precision and then taxied to the end of the line of airplanes, parking them right in front of us. Alan suggested we wait and perhaps we could talk with the pilots when they climbed out of their cockpits. Soon enough, they climbed out and we received the shock of our lives. The three pilots took off their flying helmets and shook out their hair—yes—shook out their hair! Three girls, two brunettes and a blonde, strode confidently toward us. We were speechless!

That was our introduction to the W.A.S.P.s—the Women's Air Service Pilots. We learned they deliver all sorts of airplanes all over the country and, that basically, they could fly anything in the AAF. After the girls left, Pete summed it up: "If those girls can fly a Mustang, then I sure can. I'm not letting a bunch of girls show ME up!" We laughed, but I suspect, in our hearts, we all agreed!

Training went on at a feverish pace. During that time, we also learned something else: Arizona's reputation for being hot is well-earned and our calculation of "density altitude" became even more important. We also learned that we weren't really *near* Phoenix; we were actually nearest to Goodyear, Arizona. Goodyear? I wondered how it got that name and soon found out it was quite logical. Years earlier, the Goodyear tire company was seeking a location to grow high-quality long-fiber cotton to be used in their tires. They planted hundreds of acres of cotton and soon a small town was born; what better than to name it after the company. But I was far too busy to frequent the few amusements available in Goodyear, and I only got to Phoenix once. But the flying was all-consuming.

According to my log book, I first flew a P-51 on June 23, 1943. It was a revelation! Whatever lingering skepticism I might have harbored regarding the Mustang evaporated like a snowball in the Arizona heat. Sleek, fast, easy to fly, maneuverable—what a joy! What followed was a repeat of our P-47 learning, only tailored to the P-51: study-quiz-fly-repeat. Practice, practice, practice! We spent ten weeks becoming so familiar with the Mustang that it came to feel less like we were climbing into an airplane and more like the airplane was a part of us. We especially had fun challenging each other to "tail-chases"—or dogfighting practice. We'd been playing that way since right after we first soloed in Primary, but now it really meant something.

The gunnery ranges were quite nearby in the desert and that made it easy as we practiced extensive air-to-air and air-to-ground shooting. I had one major concern, though. Our Mustangs were P-51B models and they had only four fifty-caliber machine guns in their wings as opposed to the eight guns of a P-47. It felt like hunting rabbits with a BB gun as opposed to a big-bore shotgun but, oh, well. Even four 'fifties could do a huge amount of damage. Nonetheless, gunnery practice was fun!

As we progressed through the latter part of our preparation, we also began to prepare for our transfer to England. The entire squadron was going, including the administrative people, the support people, our armament men, and the maintenance folks. The rest of the Fighter Group was already in England and they had overall organization already in place; we were just taking our squadron-level people and stuff. We would leave the airplanes behind to train the next group of pilots. Happily, the twenty-five pilots of the squadron blended well and strong friendships developed. No one washed out or crashed and we all successfully reached the end of our formal fighter transition and gunnery training. It was time to pack—we were going to war.

OVER THERE

Getting there WASN'T half the fun. The ground echelon packed equipment and files and loaded them onto a train and then they, too, rode the train as it headed east. We pilots climbed into another C-47 and endured the discomfort and noise as we also headed eastward towards our debarkation point. We ended up in a new, nearly finished barracks (that means bare studs and tarpaper again) somewhere in New Jersey. We were trapped there for a week (I say "trapped" because we were not allowed to go off base. I suppose we might have told a spy we were going to England...) before we loaded up again, this time in the ever-present "Army truck" and rode what seemed like all over the east coast before ending up on a pier sticking out into the water. I learned the water was New York's East River. Along one side of the pier was a warehouse and on the other a huge gray wall. As we exited the truck, I was shocked to see that the "huge gray wall" was actually the side of a giant ship towering over us. I'm from Oklahoma and I'd never seen a real ship, let alone something this big! We marched along the pier and joined an endless line of soldiers impatiently waiting to go aboard. I overheard someone say he ship was called "The Gray Ghost", but that didn't mean anything to me.

We did eventually get aboard and got settled into a cramped cabin built for two but occupied by eight of us. Later, the great foghorn-sounding whistle blasted and away we went. I later learned that the ship's real name was the Queen Mary, that she was called the Gray Ghost because she could steam so fast, and that there were approximately 12,000 of us aboard. I'll save the story of our boat ride for another time, but we reached Liverpool,

England on September 2, 1943, and Major Stafford got us rounded up and we headed off to board a train to London.

The trip had begun under a hot, blue, Arizona sky and ended under a dull, gray, wet-looking English one. But the weather, the strange port, and the people who spoke a different kind of English—those were only the surface differences. I experienced a deeply disturbing difference within myself. It started unexpectedly as we hiked through the dock facilities towards the town. We turned a corner and were met with unbelievable destruction. Literally, not one stone stood upon another. Stafford asked a passing workman if they were enlarging the dock and he received a sharp response.

"No, Yank, this where the *Malakand* was tied up." (As though that should mean something to us.) Our blank looks seemed to anger the man. "You Yanks! You sat back and let us fight the war alone for two years, you took all our money to buy equipment and left us broke, and now you show up all bright and happy, ready to win the war all by yourselves! Aghh!" He stalked off.

Rather abashed, Major Stafford commented; "Well. Not the warmest welcome, was it?"

We risked asking another fellow a little later about what the *Malakand* was and we learned it was ship that, back in May of '41, was filled with munitions destined for the Middle East. An air raid caught her at dockside and when she exploded, it wiped out that entire area of the docks. I began to realize that this wasn't Oklahoma, or Texas, or Arizona anymore.

We reached a train stop and eventually climbed aboard a train that seemed strange to us because it wasn't like our trains at home. The passenger car had compartments rather than rows of seats. It seemed smaller, too. As we pulled out away from the crowding buildings we could see more of what the Liverpool area looked like. We'd hardly started moving when our attention was drawn to a neighborhood of homes on a nearby hill.

Bobby Washburn noted, "Wow! Look at that neighborhood over there. They must have had a big fire—all the houses are burned down!"

Major Stafford spoke quietly: "No, Washburn, they didn't have a fire—they had Germans."

We finally realized that the damage we were seeing, that the missing buildings all around us, were evidence of the war. Bobby exclaimed in shock, "They blew up HOUSES!?" We hadn't fully thought about the war in terms of damage and death. We had been locked in our personal cocoon of concentrating on learning to fly, of passing tests, of doing our best in our very narrow world of training. We'd seen the headlines, of course, but they were about people and places we'd never heard of and no connection with. This new awareness was stunning.

The Conductor passed through the car and Elmer pointed out a building that was once a beautiful structure but was now mostly rubble.

"Sir," he inquired, "What was that building?" The railway man looked where Elmer was pointing and then answered with sadness, and a tinge of anger, "Lad, that was the Mill Road Hospital. The Huns dropped some high explosive that landed right on the maternity ward—killed six mothers and their newborn babies."

I felt like throwing up. This sudden onslaught of horror was more than I could manage all at one time.

The train ride to London was confusing. As we passed along, much of what we saw was just beautiful English countryside and then, suddenly, more carnage and rubble. Major Stafford explained that some of what we were seeing was actual targets for the Germans, but other times it was a simple locale that suffered when the German bombers just jettisoned their loads regardless of what was beneath. The destruction got worse as we neared London.

I can't explain how deeply this all affected me. Of course I knew the war was raging and, of course, I knew there was death and destruction. I hadn't considered the randomness of it, though. I had learned that we, the Americans, pursued a plan of precision *strategic* bombing of specific factories, ships, and other military targets. Bombing houses and hospitals and city- centers just did not make any sense to me. These were *people,* civilians, not soldiers. It was deeply disturbing. What is the purpose of this war? Who is really fighting it? Will we end up destroying all of civilization? What will happen to me?

We rolled through the suburbs and into the city and we saw devastation everywhere. Although the "Blitz" had occurred back in the spring and summer of 1940 and the most recent attacks had happened across England in mid-1942, I was astounded by the widespread destruction that was still visible everywhere. Huge areas of buildings were simply gone and the shells of large structures reached into the dismal sky like the lifeless fingers of a skeleton. I imagined if this was Oklahoma City—and it made me shiver.

We spent the night in London in some sort of YMCA-like building where the sign said "Transient Officers Facility". We even ate there because we had no idea how to get around London and we didn't want to get lost. The next morning, after his meetings at 8th Fighter Command, Major Stafford gathered us together and filled us in on our immediate future.

"O.K., fellows, here's the scoop. We'll be sharing an RAF field with some British folks but mostly with the other squadrons of our 336th Fighter Group and another of our groups that's on the way, the 339th Fighter group. It's in a place called "Fowlmere", which is near Cambridge. Our new airplanes are here in England, but they haven't been assembled and made ready for flight yet. They're guessing probably a month before we have them all. We're getting P-51 "B"s and "C"s, just like we trained on in Arizona."

Elmer raised his hand. "Sir, I hope someone figures out how to give us better visibility to the rear. That's where an enemy will be and we can't see them!"

Stafford nodded. "I know what you mean, but I don't know of anything yet." The Captain went on: "We'll spend the next couple of weeks getting settled and preparing for the arrival of our ground people. We'll be living in something called a "Nissen Hut". It's made of corrugated steel bent into a semicircle, sort of like half a great big sewer pipe laid on its side."

Pete asked: "Not in a barracks?"

"Nope. I guess these are faster and cheaper."

Stafford went on: "We have lots more training to do (many groans from the group at this!) because we don't know how to communicate using the British systems. Nor do we have any idea about flying in England. There are so many groups developing here that the sky is going to get very crowded. And...the weather here is almost always bad, and we don't have much experience with that. So we'll be busy for a while before we 'take to the sky in search of the dreaded Hun'."

We smiled ruefully.

The phrase "busy for a while" contained more meaning than we first understood. When we transferred to Fowlmere, the RAF facilities had been up and going for some time, and the other squadrons of 336th were moving along with the group facilities and with their squadron needs, but our squadron facilities were best described as "non-existent." There was one hut ready for us pilots, but there were piles of corrugated steel pieces that needed to be assembled into the rest of the huts. Fortunately, there were engineering troops on-site who were hastily assembling and anchoring the huts so we pilots, at least, didn't find ourselves with wrenches in hand. We actually spent a lot of time with our counterparts in the 336th, setting up systems for everything from training schedules to lists of radio frequencies and a mind-boggling collection of other minutiae. Our goal was to have as much ready as possible for when the rest of our folks arrived. We learned a lot, but our lessons were not only related to the inner workings of an AAF fighter group.

The weather was vastly different from Arizona: the locals expressed pleasure about how warm it had been recently, but we were freezing. The high temps had been in the upper 50s and the lows in the upper 30s. Brrr! Then a series of thunderstorms came through and drenched the field and we received our first introduction to English mud. It was made worse, of course, by the torn up state of construction around us, but that made it no less gooey. And this was only September!

We were also learning another language. George Bernard Shaw's observation that the "The United States and England are two great nations separated only by a common language" really proved true. For example: the common "hood"/"bonnet"/"trunk"/"boot" confusion. But others such as we call it a "sidewalk", but they call it "pavement". An important one is we call it an "eraser", but they call it a "rubber". (That one could get someone in a lot of trouble!) We learned that a "faucet" is a "tap", that "potato chips" are "crisps", and that our "subway" is their "tube" or "metro" whereas their "subway" is a pedestrian tunnel. It was fun and funny but also very important.

As our preparations improved and our knowledge got better, the weather got worse. As the weather got colder and wetter, we began to despair of being able to fly in it. We'd done a minimum bit of instrument and night flying in our training, but the English weather was getting progressively worse and we weren't prepared for bad weather flying. Obviously, when our airplanes arrived, we'd need a lot of bad weather practice.

And then things really started to happen. One afternoon early in October, several trucks pulled in and our ground people and all the equipment finally arrived. Getting everything set up kept us running for a few days, but at least we didn't feel so much like orphans. The 501st Fighter Squadron was becoming a reality. Then the day we had longed for—on Wednesday, November 3, 1943, we were notified to report to the maintenance depot to pick up our airplanes! Hooray!

Flying "home" to Fowlmere immediately showed us some unexpected problems. Although the weather that day was surprisingly good, we took off in groups of four and we quickly learned our radios didn't work properly. We could sort of communicate with each other, but what we mostly heard was static and buzzing; and we could sort of communicate with Fowlmere Tower through the same static and buzzing, but we absolutely could NOT communicate with the British air controllers. This was an extremely serious problem and our headquarters immediately sent radio technicians to us. It turned out that our radios need some kind of suppressors and other electronic wizardry but, even worse, we learned the British were using highly effective "very high frequency" radios (called "VHF" radios) whereas we were using only "high frequency" (HF) radios and ours were not at all compatible with theirs. After a few days of flurried activity we ended up with highly effective VHF radios. Were they British or American? I don't know, but they worked marvelously.

This was when we also received the assignment of our airplane, our flight assignments, and the permanent assignment of our ground crew. I felt truly blessed in all. I was selected by Major Stafford to fly as the leader of Red Flight with Jim Weatherby as my wingman. I was "Red Leader" with Jim as "Red Two". "Red Three" was Ben "PK" Johnson with "Reb" Grantham as his wingman ("Red Four"). Our squadron code was "AP" and my airplane was "J", so I was "AP+J".

My crew chief was Technical Sergeant Joseph Pistorelli, from Piscataway, New Jersey. He had been in the air force for many years, had short-cropped gray hair, and was probably 45 years old. He wanted me to call him "pistol", but I just naturally settled into "Pappy", which he accepted with reluctant grace. My Armorer was Corporal Leonard Watkins, 22, from some unpronounceable town in Wisconsin, and my general mechanic was Private Lawrence   Priestman, 21, from St. Joseph, Missouri. They were good guys and made a great team. It didn't take long for them to let me know that "the J-bird" was THEIR airplane and I was to treat it accordingly. I figured that my life depended on that airplane and the guys could claim it if they wanted—just keep it flying and fighting!

While we were busy getting started up, some very big things were happening around us. Beginning in August, 1942, bombers of our 8th Air Force had started attacking targets in occupied countries in Western Europe. These first missions were actually viewed as experiments intended to prove the viability of our precision daylight bombing plan. The first few went quite well, but as the Germans responded with increasing ferocity, the later attacks had been a bit less spectacular, although still considered successful. All the way through the winter and into 1943, the size of our available bombing force grew remarkably and missions continued into enemy territory despite some frightful weather. There were some lessons learned that directly impacted us. The original theory that the B-17s and B-24s could defend themselves had suffered in the reality of determined attacks by swarms of German fighters. It soon became apparent that fighter protection was necessary, but there were problems in that area also. The earliest missions had been supported by British Spitfires because we didn't have enough fighters over here yet to fly our own. The Spitfire is a fabulous airplane, but it was designed as a *defensive* airplane, intended to protect England from attack and, therefore, having a short range. Its success in the Battle of Britain was evidence of the Spits' abilities, but because of its short range the penetration of the early bombing missions was limited. The problem now, though, was we needed an *offensive* fighter with a long enough range to accompany the bombers deep into enemy territory. And not only long range was needed—the escort fighter also needed to be able to fly and fight at the high altitudes where the bombers flew. As we finally built up sufficient forces, we had the P-47 and the P-38. Both were fast and could fly high, and both offered a longer range than the Spitfire, but neither offered the truly long range needed to properly protect the bombers. That led to us. The Merlin-engined P-51 offered enough range to go as far on internal fuel as a P-47 could go even with external tanks. We were also fast and could fly high so it was desired that we get the Mustangs into service as quickly as possible. Our 501st squadron was not the first in combat—a group in the neighboring 9th Air Force was borrowed by the 8th and they held that honor. They were quickly proving the value of our wonderful airplane.

Meanwhile, we spent our time training—training in bad weather flying, training in cooperation with the British air controllers, training in how to rendezvous with the bombers at a precise point and a precise time and even training in our combat tactics.

SARAH

Late in November our planes were down for maintenance and we were granted a long weekend off; nearly all of us from the 501st headed for London. The other guys were in search of excitement, but all I wanted to do was find some warm clothes. I had seen some of the RAF guys wearing a heavy knit sweater and I thought something like that might keep me from freezing. Outside the train station I hailed a cab and asked him to take me to a department store and he did—a store called Harrods. I soon learned that Harrods is world-famous and if you can't find what you want at Harrods, it probably doesn't exist. I went to the men's department and soon found myself purchasing not only a heavy sweater like I'd seen, but also some heavy knit socks and some "thermal underwear" that back home we'd called "long- johns". I paid for my purchases and they were wrapped and bundled into a large paper carry bag. As I left the department, I was lost in wonder at the vast array of things Harrods had to offer, despite the war and its restrictions. I was looking at a display on my left as I approached an intersection of the shopping aisles and I didn't see, until too late, a moving stack of boxes coming from my right. You guessed it—I collided with the moving stack and boxes and parcels went flying. I grunted as we collided and the person carrying the stack made a noise also. I hurriedly bent to help retrieve the scattered boxes and while doing so, I looked up to apologize to the other shopper. I looked into the most captivating amber eyes I could ever have imagined—sort of a coppery-yellowy color. Before I could apologize, the lady spoke:

"You oaf! Don't you watch where you're going?!" This was said with a lovely English accent.

I had to stop staring at her eyes, but the rest of her lovely face didn't help my equilibrium much.

"I, uh, I'm…" I was stammering as though I was struck dumb—which I guess I was!

"Well, don't just kneel there and splutter, help me pick all this up!"

I hastened to milady's bidding.

I finally recovered enough to speak.

"Look, miss, I'm terribly sorry. I was looking the other way and I didn't see you coming."

"That figures! Another Yank who doesn't know which way to look before crossing the street! God help us if you don't all kill yourselves before you ever go to fight!"

I was regaining my composure now and I was actually finding her caustic comments a bit much.

"I said I'm sorry and I'm picking up packages as fast as I can. I certainly did not knock into you on purpose. In addition, I'm sorry you have such a low opinion of Americans, but we'll eventually learn that things are different here! Thank you for your patience!" Yes, my tone was a bit sharp.

She paused before responding and I used the respite to restack her towering pile and prepare to hand it to her.

I also took the opportunity to slip in another comment:

"In my own defense, I don't know how you can see over all this stuff to see where you're going. Nonetheless, here…" and I reached out the stack for her to take it.

I was left standing there awkwardly proffering the pile which she did not take from me. Instead, she laughed.

"Well, you're a spunky one, anyway. And, yes, it is piled too high and I can't see where I'm going—so I suppose I'm as much at fault as you."

I was feeling distinctly embarrassed standing there holding out the pile of goods into empty space, so I set them gently back on the floor. Actually, it did seem rather humorous that neither of us could have seen the other. I chuckled, too:

"O.K, it seems our collision was pre-ordained or something. Is there anything in all this stuff that might have broken?"

Her smile excited every molecule in my suddenly jelly-like body. *Wow,* I thought to myself, *she is the most beautiful women I have ever seen!*

"No, all clothing and soft things. I'm glad I didn't buy the expensive vase I was considering!"

"Oh, my! I'm glad, too," I smiled, "because I probably couldn't afford to replace an expensive vase!"

She looked at my uniform.

"So I see you're wearing flyer's wings—are you driving one of those big bombers I keep seeing overhead?"

"No. I'm a fighter pilot and I will soon be escorting those big bombers to Germany."

"I see." And then; "I don't know you fellow's ranks—what does your one bar mean?"

"I'm a second lieutenant in the U.S. Army Air Force." I decided I'd try to impress her a little. "I'm a flight leader in the 501st fighter squadron."

Her answer surprised me. "I don't think you're supposed to tell me that—there are rumored to be German spies all over London."

I colored in embarrassment. "Oh. Uh, yes, I suppose you're right. Forget I said that, OK?"

"All right, I promise. But I'm serious about the spies."

We stood there in the aisle talking for quite a while. I found out her name is Sarah Brockman, that her brother is a Sub-Lieutenant in the Royal Navy, and that she is not married.

"Well, Mr. Peters, I really should be going. I've been expected back at the office for over an hour."

"Sarah, please let me help you carry some of this stuff. I'd hate for you to be hit by a bus because you didn't see it coming!"

She thought about it for a minute, and then gave in to the logic of my suggestion.

"Well, all right...'Tommy', is it?"

"Yes, Thomas J. Peters, at your command."

"Well, then," she laughed, "my command is we divide this stuff up and get me back to work!"

Fortunately it wasn't raining and she led us off to walk rather than try to hail a cab. We walked several blocks, making various turns, and I was completely lost. We'd walked about ten minutes when she entered a tall office building. I didn't even get the address. I did note that we rode the elevator to the eighth floor, exited, went down a long hallway and finally entered an office on the right that had "Wooster and Smith Creations" lettered on the door.

Hmm, I wondered, what do "Wooster and Smith" create? I would eventually find out.

Sarah led me through a reception area where a matronly-looking, gray-haired woman commanded the desk. We passed through a door and entered what must have been a typing pool—probably a dozen girls hammering away on

81

typewriters, and then through a door lettered "S. Brockman, Creative Director". Ah, Ha!

We piled the purchases carefully in a corner and then Sarah came to me and offered her hand.

"Thank you, Thomas Peters, you have been most helpful."

I looked again into those captivating eyes, this time showing a hint of mirth, and I melted all over again.

"You're welcome Miss Brockman. May I ask a question?" I wanted to find out about the "creative" stuff.

She laughed playfully. "Yes, I will have dinner with you."

I was floored! I guess it was obvious because she hesitated, saying:

"That IS what you were going to ask me, wasn't it?"

I'm no fool and I adjusted quickly. "Why, of course!" I laughed. "Which just shows that great minds DO think alike."

Because I knew absolutely nothing about London, she suggested a small Italian restaurant near her apartment, and she then wrote out directions and the address. I hadn't even arranged a hotel for myself yet, so I faced a busy afternoon.

Need I mention I was excited?

Dinner was wonderful. Talking and laughing, Sarah and I started to become better acquainted. I found her to be a smart, capable woman who also happened to be breathtakingly beautiful. It was at dinner when I learned that Sarah was in charge of creating advertising copy for use on BBC radio programs and in various printed materials. Due to the war, there wasn't really much to advertise, so many of the "ads" were actually public service announcements. It sounded fascinating to me. In addition, I was, of course, curious how such a perfect woman could be "unattached", but it seemed rude to ask. She answered my unasked question:

"This war is awful," she stated. "There is so much death and destruction and we have all been touched by it. Two years ago, my brother introduced me to one of his university professors and we hit it off. We spent a lot of time together and were falling rather seriously in love. During the summer holidays last year, he went home to visit his family in Hull and he was there when the Germans bombed the city. Their house suffered a direct hit and he and his parents were killed."

I didn't know what to say. I had never known how to respond when people suffered a death in the family and this was even worse. I guess she could see my discomfort, because she reached across and touched my hand.

"Don't be distressed. This has happened to so many of us we just know how to respond. Thank you for obviously caring."

I then wondered about how to proceed.

"Sarah, I DO care and I'm just learning how really awful this war is. So far, for me, it's all been training and learning and moving. The horrible reality is just setting in. I'm sorry for your loss. But I also have a selfish question: I have never enjoyed being with someone as much as I have enjoyed being with you tonight. So my question is, how do I move forward with you? Or, maybe I should ask, MAY I move forward with you?"

I wonder if was really holding my breath, or if it just seemed like it...

Sarah was quiet and thoughtful for quite a while.

"Well," she finally responded, "I'm not certain. I, too, have enjoyed our time together tonight. You are a really nice person. We seem to have similar interests and outlooks, and even our senses of humor are similar. Normally, I would enjoy getting better acquainted, but life isn't normal. You are in the service, and you will soon be in very deadly situations and, frankly, I don't think I could handle another loss like losing John. At the same time, I enjoy your company. You are a bright and fascinating person." She paused thoughtfully again. "Why don't we try this: you call me when you can and we'll try to get together from time-to-time? Not trying for anything serious, but just having fun together. What do you think?"

I was impressed by her serious approach and I told her so.

"Sarah, I appreciate your thoughtful response. Of course I understand and I agree with you. I WILL call you, probably every chance I get!" I laughed. "And I'm so new here that I don't know what our routines will be, but I would love to spend every minute with you that you will allow. It seems to me that being 'just friends' with you will be a wonderful gift. Yes, let's just have fun."

We ended our evening by taking a cab back to her apartment. She gave me a note with her telephone number and address, we shared one light kiss goodnight, and she went inside. Fortunately, the cab driver knew how to get me back to my hotel.

THE BIG LEAGUES

The weather was so bad through December and into January that we didn't get to fly much--enough to remember how, but not enough to become really sharp in the important lessons pertaining to the war. Meanwhile, the bombers squeezed in missions on the few marginally flyable days with mixed success. They learned that precision bombing wasn't possible when the weather obscured the target. There were stories of a new radar-bombing technique, but that wasn't working all that well, either. One thing about the bad weather—it seemed to keep the German fighters on the ground, so our combat losses were minimal. But when the Luftwaffe did come up, they were deadly and bomber losses were terrible. The word throughout the Eighth was that the long-range P-51s were the answer. We were eager to participate, but our leaders still felt we needed added training. But there soon came a time when the need was so great, it was decided that we could get the rest of our training while flying actual missions. Wow! That's what I call "on-the-job training"!

The 501st Fighter Squadron flew its first combat mission on January 7, 1944 as escorts for over 500 bombers to Ludwigshafen, Germany. The weather was very cloudy and the bombers tried the radar-bombing technique. They were somewhat successful; the 501st was not. We did not see a single enemy airplane. Frankly, I wasn't heartbroken about that. We'd had difficulty from the beginning. We were awakened at 4 AM and trudged through the mud to a delightful breakfast of powdered eggs and Spam. Then we went for our first-ever mission briefing where we learned where we going, what courses to fly, and what radio frequencies to use. Following that, we jumped on jeeps for a ride through the worst of the mud to our airplanes. Pappy greeted me and reported that all was well with the "J-bird" and the guys wished me success by commenting "We're ready to paint some swastikas on here, so go get 'em!" Their encouragement just deepened my apprehension.

We took off and were immediately surrounded by the deep gloom of the low clouds over the base. When we broke through into the clear air on top, we were scattered all over the place. I finally got my Red Flight rounded up and we managed to join Major Stafford and the rest as they straggled into position. That made us a couple of minutes late in joining the bombers, so we cranked on some speed to catch up. That used up extra fuel, and fuel was precious on such a long flight. Things finally settled down for a while and we droned along flying a weaving pattern for top cover for the bomber elements at the rear end of the long train of B-17s and   B-24s. It took a lot of my attention to stay in position as we weaved above the "Big Friends", as we called the bombers. I wondered how I was supposed to do that and look for enemy fighters at the same time.

When we went "feet wet", or "landfall out", that meant we were over the English Channel. When we went "landfall in", that meant we were over the European continent, which was enemy territory, and we could expect enemy fighters at any time. I was very anxious and hyper-alert. The weather was so bad, though, that no enemy planes showed up and we kept on going. All the way to the target, we were not challenged. The bombers made their drops through the clouds and we all turned for home. We were hoping the Germans would come up, but the few that did were somewhere away from us and we didn't see any. It was a long ride home.

On January 11, the weather improved enough for us to go out again. This time there were 663 bombers heading for Germany. We didn't fly across the Channel with them but were supposed to rendezvous with them just before they reached the target. That was as far as the P-47s could go, and we were supposed to take over and protect the bombers over the target. We must have been too eager because we arrived a bit early and, again, used up precious fuel waiting to rendezvous. The target was several aircraft manufacturing plants in the general vicinity of Berlin. We stayed with the lead element of the main force attacking Oschersleben, location of a major builder of the FW-190 fighter. Unfortunately, the weather had closed in and most of our attacking force was recalled, but the 1st Bombardment Group was already so close to the target that they went ahead with the attack despite the weather. The Germans responded in mass. Maybe they thought we were going to Berlin or something, but it looked to me like the entire Luftwaffe came up against us. We few P-51s were vastly outnumbered, which is both bad and good. Bad because there are many more of them than us and that puts us at a great disadvantage. Good because we certainly didn't lack for targets!

The first time I ever fired my guns in actual combat was at an ME-109 that was crossing in front of me from my right to my left. I turned to line up a deflection shot at him and I had just pressed the trigger when Jim, my ever-faithful wingman, shouted into the radio: "Lucky! Break Right! Break Right!" In such a situation, one does NOT question, "Why, Jim?" or "Really, Jim?" One does what one is told— right now! I broke right just in time for an FW-190 to zoom past me on the left. I immediately banked back in and tried to get a shot at him. I was firing, but if I hit him it didn't show. I broke off and saw another 109 making a run on a Mustang, so I swung over to try to chase him away. I couldn't get really close, so I fired from about 300 yards out. I might have hit him because he broke and dove away, but I certainly didn't seriously wound him. By this time, there were dogfights all over the sky but it was clear that the fighters weren't interested in us, they wanted the bombers who had now finished bombing and were heading for England. Despite all the crazy fighting with airplanes zooming and diving and turning, I suddenly found myself off to the edge of the fighting. With Jim still stuck to me (What a guy!), I turned and tried to regain the fight. In the moments before I rejoined I could see the whole sweep of the battle: in the left distance, a B-17 was spiraling down with one wing shot off; on the right was a fighter—I couldn't tell whose—arcing into a dive with flames trailing behind it; everywhere I looked I saw airplanes twisting and turning desperately, airplanes smoking, airplanes burning; and the climax was a B-17 that was flying along when suddenly it exploded into a bright white-orange ball and then—there was no trace of the B-17. No debris, no smoke, nothing; it just ceased to exist.

The Germans finally ended their attack and we formed up for home—a good thing, too—because our fuel was getting worryingly low.

After we returned to Fowlmere, we each "debriefed" by sitting with an intelligence officer and telling him we did and what we saw. That was when I learned that Major Stafford had downed a 109 for the first kill for the 501st. I was very frustrated with my own performance. I scattered a few bullets around and didn't do a bit of good and I was really kicking myself! I also learned that the other P-51 group had claimed fifteen kills and that we had suffered no fighter losses. But I was shocked to learn what had happened to the bombers: of the 139 bombers that attacked Oschersleben, 34 were shot down and of the entire attacking force of 238 bombers that hadn't heard the recall, a total of 60 were destroyed. Sixty bombers meant 600 men lost! I was still learning how brutal war really is.

After that mission, the weather really closed in and terrible weather was forecast for the next two weeks. I managed to get a three day pass and I headed for London. Before leaving, I called Sarah and she said she'd see me—at least that made me feel a lot better!

SARAH'S DESK

Sarah Brockman sat at her desk staring at the heaps of paper piled upon it.

Oh, my, she thought ruefully, *why did all the girls finish their submissions at the same time? This is hopeless!*

Sarah's position as Creative Director at Wooster and Smith was considered a "plum" job, including a good job title, a private office, high-level responsibilities, and a good salary. She enjoyed a strong trust with both Wooster and with Smith and, best of all, she enjoyed her job. But now she had to make sense out of this mountain of paper.

Well, she thought determinedly, *it won't go away by itself, so I'd best wade in.*

She'd been at it for about an hour and she was deep into an editorial analysis of a piece submitted by Beatrice Whiting with the hopeful title of "Draw your Stocking Lines Straight Without a Ruler". Sarah was unsure about how seriously to take the piece. It was certainly true that real stockings had been long unavailable and the process of duplicating the stocking seams by drawing them on was common practice. At the same time, however, she wondered whether such a weighty tome was worthy of the ink it would take to publish it. That was when her secretary, the matronly Mrs. Breese that I had noted on my earlier visit, buzzed Sarah's intercom to announce that Sarah had a call on line two.

Sarah was perturbed at having her line of thought broken and responded irritably, "Who is it, please?"

"It's Lieutenant Peters of the American Air Corps."

"Oh. Thank you." Sarah paused before picking up the call. She like Tom Peters and she enjoyed their infrequent telephone conversations. But those were personal calls and she didn't like being interrupted at work. *I'll have to set that straight,* she thought. She punched line two and answered rather brusquely:

"Sarah Brockman, how may I help you?"

"Hello, Sarah, it's Tom Peters. Look, I know I shouldn't bother you at work and I apologize, but I just got a surprise three-day pass and I'm just leaving the base and heading for London. May I call you when I get there? Maybe we can get together or something?"

Well, I guess I don't have to scold him after all. Get together? I have some free time...

"So, Lieutenant Peters, when do you expect to arrive?"

"Well, the so-called schedule says 4:45 PM, but that might be more of a guess than a promise."

Sarah laughed. "Are you aware, Lieutenant Peters, that there is a war on? And that the safe arrival of a train of face cloths might be more vital to the war effort than the timely delivery of a handsome young flyer?"

I couldn't help but chuckle. "Face cloths? Really?"

"Yes, sir. I personally sat in a crowded train, waiting in a side track, for a train filled with vitally needed face cloths to pass by." We were both were laughing now.

"Yes, Tom, why don't you come the office when you get here? I have a mountain of work to get through, so I'm sure I'll still be here."

"Great! See you then!"

After she hung up, Sarah found herself thinking about Tom, which led her to ponder the future, which led her to remember the past.

Growing up in Westcliff-on-Sea was wonderful. A well-heeled community where my father could have a successful practice as a barrister. How I miss those fun summer days of playing in the surf, sailing in the Thames estuary, and shopping with my mother. I'm thankful the Germans have no interest in bombing such a small resort town.

Sarah was startled to find herself doodling—pictures of stocking seams!

Well, that's a story for the brain researchers! Stockings, indeed! Her musings continued with reminiscences from her university days at University College London. *It's so sad that so much of the college has been destroyed in the bombings—what a waste! I never had so much fun in school as I did there. I'll always remember Dr. Francis in the Creative Writing course—the memories still make me smile—'Make it come alive, Sarah, make it come alive!' That's where I developed my love of the written word. The Great English Novel someday? Maybe, who knows?*

Sarah rocked back in her chair, lost in the fog of memory.

Billy Hesmith. Lord, I haven't thought about Billy in ages! That little rascal just loved to make me shriek. The day he hid a live frog in my book bag about did me in—imagine, dying of a heart attack at age nine! The last I heard, he was on convoy patrol in a corvette. I hope he's still alive... That led to more recent, and more painful, thoughts. *John. John Beeman with the ready smile and the hearty laugh. John who tried so hard to grow a beard in order to look more "professorial", and ended up looking like a sweet boy with a fuzzy face. The sweet boy who stole my heart with his warm eyes and deep gentleness.*

Sarah rocked forward and slammed her fists onto her desktop, unwanted tears flowing down her reddened cheeks. "Oh, GOD, how I HATE this war!"

****

There must have been a lot of face cloths going to London because the advertised 4:45 PM arrival turned out to be a little after 5:30. The taxi kept me dry until I reached Sarah's building, but simply crossing the sidewalk was enough to drench me. Did I mention how much I enjoy English weather?

When I dripped my way into the office, the matronly, gray-haired lady was still ensconced at her desk. I thought I'd try the 'friendly smile' tactic to win her over.

"Hello!" I greeted her with my cheeriest tone and biggest smile.

She responded with a single nod.

Well, I thought, *so much for the friendly smile!*

"Miss Brockman is expecting me…"

Another single nod and a slight tip of the head towards the door leading through the typing pool and on to Sarah's office.

"Thank you." With another cheery smile.

As I opened the door into the typing pool, I didn't hear the clatter of typewriters but, instead, the cacophony of many female voices. Apparently, 5:30 must be quitting time because all of the women were shrugging into coats, hefting purses, and doing other sorts of female departure rituals. As I opened the door and stepped inside, the room went suddenly and totally silent.

"Whoa!" I exclaimed. I was shocked at the sudden change and was completely taken aback. I tried to think quickly, finally saying: "Hello, ladies. Is it something I said?"

That elicited a few smiles. One of the girls, probably one of the more adventurous, timidly asked with a smile: "So, you must be Miss Brockman's latest beau." The others seemed to be listening closely.

I smiled. "Well, I would dearly love to be Miss Brockman's latest beau but, actually, we're just friends."

"You're the American flight leader aren't you?"

I guess Sarah had told them a little about me.

"Yes. Unless she has other flight leader friends, that would be me. My Name is Tom..."

That seemed to open the door to excited conversation and soon questions were flying at me faster than I could answer.

"You fly a fighter?" "Where are you based?" "Where do you come from?" "Why are the Americans so cute?"

That last one made me blush but Sarah opened her office door just in time to save me.

"Thank you, ladies, you can go home now."

As the girls passed me, I received various smiles, curious looks, and even a couple of winks.

Boy, am I out of my league! I thought ruefully.

As the last of the girls left, Sarah spoke.

"Hello, Lieutenant Peters."

"Hello, Miss Brockman."

"I see you arrived safely."

"Yes. Despite the critically needed face cloths that delayed our arrival, I am here in sound, but slightly dampened, condition."

Sarah smiled, but I noted her reddened eyes, as though she'd been crying. That caused me great concern—was there some problem?

"Well, come on in. I have to straighten up the piles on my desk and then we can go."

As I sat across her desk from her, I noticed the doodles of women's legs.

"Why, Sarah, I see you have a fascination with women's legs..." I joked as I pointed to the doodles.

She smiled with a blush. "Actually, it's not some weird fetish. One of the girls submitted a proposed newspaper article about stockings and I guess it stuck in my mind."

We both chuckled, but I couldn't help but be concerned by her red eyes and depressed tone, so I boldly asked her about it.

"Well," she responded, "if you must know, I've been sitting here having a personal pity party. I was remembering better times and I have, yet, again, reached the astounding conclusion that I hate this war! I wonder if it will ever end, and I wonder if any of us will survive to have a life afterwards."

She was starting to tear up again.

"You've been thinking about John?"

She looked up sharply. "Of, course!"

"Whoa, Sarah! I'm not criticizing you! I am so filled with sympathy for you, and for all of you who have suffered so much. I am astounded at the spirit that keeps you all going. You inspire me! And that seems to me to be the reason we're fighting this war. The people who inflict this kind of suffering and loss on innocent people must be stopped!"

Sarah was quiet and gazed deeply at me.

"Tom Peters, you are a noble man."

It was my turn to color. "No, Sarah, I just want to live in a world where I can marry the girl I love and where we can raise our children in a safe and wholesome environment and give them a chance for a successful future. I guess that's selfish, but this evil around us MUST be stopped, and I'll do my best to help stop it."

Sarah was quiet again, then, forcing a smile, said:

"Tom, I need a jolt of good medicine. Do you know what would be the best possible medicine for me right now?"

I had no idea.

"The medicine I need right now is for you to take me to dinner and tell me stories of your ranch in Oklahoma and about those crazy cowboys you have!"

And that is what we did.

Finding a decent meal in London was challenging. The convoys were beginning to get through and there was a bit more to eat, but it certainly wasn't easy to find a "gourmet" meal. We finally settled for a small café a few blocks from Sarah's office. I launched into every cowboy story I could think of and, I hope I might be forgiven if I embellished them a bit, but Sarah needed to laugh. As we talked, I watched her carefully and the "medicine" seemed to work and Sarah began to brighten and become more of her warm and glowing self.

As I was gazing at her, it occurred to me that I have mentioned Sarah's unique amber eyes, but I haven't described the rest her. I'm not very good at this, but here goes: Sarah is a few inches shorter than I am, and I am just under six feet tall. I couldn't (and wouldn't!) begin to guess her weight, but she is VERY well assembled with all the perfect curves in all the right places. Her hair is light brown and hangs to about her shoulders. Her hair style is smooth on top with the ends curled under (I have no idea what that's called!). She has the smoothest skin I have ever seen. Her face is rather oval-shaped. Her eyes are large, her nose is cute, and her lips are perfect for kissing.

That's certainly not the best description, but it's the best I can do. Summarized in one word: Beautiful!

It was well after 9 PM when we left the café and that's when I learned something else about life in London. We had hardly stepped out the door when loud sirens started sounding.

"Oh, not again!" Sarah exclaimed. "This is just ridiculous!"

"Sarah, what's going on?"

"You haven't heard the air raid sirens before?" She sounded incredulous.

"No. I guess I've been lucky. Are they still sending bombers over?"

"No. We pretty well stopped that, but now, every once in a while, they send over a couple of fighters carrying bombs."

"Good grief! What's their target?"

"London."

That's all? Just 'London'? Nothing specific?"

"No, nothing specific. I guess if their target is London, they rather can't miss, can they?"

I was stunned.

"Come on, innocent boy, let's duck into the nearest shelter just to play it safe."

As we reached the entrance to the shelter, I couldn't help but pause and look into the night sky. Bright beams of searchlights were waving across the sky, the sirens were still screaming their undulating cry, and in the distance I heard shooting.

"Sarah, is that shooting the anti-aircraft guns firing at the airplanes?"

"Yes. At least they seem far from here."

It suddenly struck me that this must be what it's like in Germany when we bomb them. Although we try to hit specific targets, the British just do their "area bombing" of city areas. And when our bombers can't see their specific targets, they just drop on the city, too. This attack was probably by two small fighters and I was frightened. Our attacks now were by up to a thousand bombers and I couldn't imagine the terror that must cause.

When we went inside, I mentioned this to Sarah and she responded with a shrug. "Tom, we didn't start this war."

Finally the "all clear" signal sounded and we went on our way.

Sarah invited me into her apartment and we ended up talking for another couple of hours. She told me about her childhood and I told her about mine. It was interesting to note the differences—and the similarities—even though we grew up several thousand miles apart in vastly different circumstances.

Thoughts of John were still too fresh in Sarah's mind for anything else to happen and I was shuffled off to my hotel—alone.

She had to work the next two days, but we did get to spend the evenings together. I was becoming increasingly fond of this warm, wonderful, smart English girl, and I realized that I fondly wished I COULD become "Sarah's latest beau". But there was a war on and my chances for winning her heart seemed immeasurably distant. Oh, well, as the old saying goes: "hope springs eternal".

BETTER WEATHER

On January 29, the weather was still awful, but not AS awful as it had been. We were able to get off from our bases in England and our fighter group met the bombers on time over Frankfurt-am-Main, known as "the Chicago of Germany". The bombers couldn't bomb visually, but they had a way of using radar to find the target. Over 500 bombers hit the industrial area of the city and, I suppose because of the bad weather over the target, we didn't meet any enemy fighters. We went out again the next day in similar conditions, again met the bombers on time, this time over Brunswick. This time we met a few fighters. It wasn't swarms of them like on the like trip to Oschersleben, but there were probably 40 or so. As we approached, I was determined to do a better job than last time. There were the single-engine 109s and 190s, but also some twin-engine fighters that stayed just out of our range and lobbed rockets into the bomber stream. They were unfortunately effective and we were so busy with the other fighters that we couldn't go chasing after them.

My first excitement came as we dove into the German fighters. I lined up on a 109 and got some good shots in. He seemed to be smoking when I had to turn away to stop another 109 from going after Reb. I just scared him away, but didn't note any damage to him. With faithful Jim at my side, we turned in on three 190s that were forming up for a frontal attack on the bombers. I got solid hits on the one on the left and Jim really clobbered the one in the middle. The one on the right peeled away. That attack carried us into the range of the bomber's guns and they couldn't tell the difference between a 109 and Mustang, so things got pretty hot for a bit. We managed to get back outside and lit off after a 109 that was trying for a diving approach from the left of the bombers. I could see what he was trying to do so I was able to anticipate his actions. I was waiting for him when he turned in and I laid some really good deflection shots that hit him hard. Lots of pieces flew off and he broke off his attack. I tossed a few more shots after him as he banked away and to my surprise, his canopy flew off and the pilot bailed out! By Jove—as the English say—I think I just got my first kill!

Immediately after that, Jim called for me to break left and, as I turned and dove away, I saw Jim take out a 190 that was too focused on me. Score one for Jim!

And then it was suddenly just American airplanes. We Mustangs formed up and caught up to the bombers so we could protect them on the way out until the P-47s met us, then we headed for home.

Our debriefing was like a party. The 336th Group scored its first big success. I was credited with one confirmed and one probable. Jim also got one confirmed and one probable. The entire group was credited with 23 confirmed and seven probables. Now it felt like we were contributing to the war, and I also felt much better about my own performance.

Four days later, we were off again. Our missions of escorting the bombers were code-named "Ramrods" and on February 3, we flew a Ramrod to Emden. As usual, I led Red Flight of the 501st with Jim as my wingman, and with PK with Reb as his wingman. We were stacked above and slightly ahead of the lead bomber box. Enemy fighters waited just out of range, waiting for us to use up our fuel so we would have to leave the bombers unprotected. Apparently, these guys didn't know much about the Mustang. With the extra fuel tank behind the seat, and droppable wing tanks under our wings, we could make Emden and hang around for quite a while. One of the enemy must have lost his patience, because he suddenly turned and raced in towards us. Major Stafford nailed him, and the guy's friends seemed to learn their lesson. The bombers bombed via radar again, and we all turned and headed for home.

On February 4th, we headed to Frankfurt again. This time, the enemy fighters were much more aggressive. They tried a new tactic of massing in numbers as a way to overwhelm us. It didn't work real well. I led Red Flight into a gaggle of about 20 single-engine fighters—the usual mix of 109s and 190s. I know it seems that four of us attacking twenty of them sounds ludicrous. But it really isn't as crazy as it seems. The four of us can pick our targets, but the twenty of them get in each other's way trying to evade us. We have a definite advantage when they are that confused. Of course, we have to make our pass and break clear because, if we hang around, they can box us in and take turns hitting us. This time, our pass worked perfectly. We drove in and they tried to scatter. Reb got one 109 and PK another. Jim got one and I got good hits on another. Then we were through and away. Let me tell you, that P-51 could zoom into a climb. Our four-bladed "paddle prop" took a good bite of air and up we went! When we climbed above the enemy, we could then do a wing-over and dive into a perfect fast pass at them again. On that second pass, a couple of them slid off to either side, trying to set up an ambush as we came down. I saw what they were doing, and I had a plan...

"Red Three and Four continue your attack on the main body. Red Two break right and attack head on into the right bunch, I'll go left. Ready? Red Flight, Break!"

If we'd been in an air show, it would have looked a little like an upside-down flower. I barreled into the left ambushers head on, moving fast. They didn't expect that and tried, too late, to break away. Now, attacking a fast-moving fighter plane head on is not for the faint of heart. I picked my target and headed straight towards his nose. He was firing and I was firing. It's like the kid's game of "chicken"—who will break first and which way will he break? If he breaks upward, I can rake his underside. If he breaks downward, I can rake his top side. Or he mine. The

102

closing rate is horrendous and it takes me much longer to tell it than it does to happen. I'd heard somewhere that the natural tendency is to break down, so I just stayed on him and bored in. I kept firing and I knew I was getting hits. Just as we reached the pucker-point where it's time to break, he blew up. My first flamer! Whew! That little episode left me sweating. If his pal had been more aggressive, he might have been able to set on me, but he disappeared instead.

Jim must have gotten through OK, too, because as I turned to join Reb and PK, here came faithful Jim, sliding in on my wing with a cheerful thumbs-up.

It is amazing how much lead can come from a B-17. And when they maintain their combat box formation, those bombers can fill the sky with a deadly hail. If any of the enemy fighters managed to get through us, they then had to brave the massed gunners of the bomber formations. I saw several planes with black crosses going down in flames.

Back at debriefing, the Group was credited with 18 confirmed and 9 probables. I got one confirmed and another probable, while Jim scored two confirmed. We were becoming more confident of our airplanes and of ourselves. I had noted that my flying was becoming instinctive. The airplane was just an extension of me, and I didn't have to think about my maneuvers, I just instinctively did what was needed.

This might be a good time to briefly explain how we were organized and to identify my bosses. The 336th Fighter Group was commanded by Colonel Henry Martinson. He was boss to my immediate boss, Major Jim Stafford, Commander of the 501st Fighter Squadron. The 336th consisted of three squadrons, the 500th, 501st, and 502nd. The entire Group consisted of about 200 people. I won't name everyone, but there are a couple of men who deserve mention. Our Doctor—Flight Surgeon, by title—is Dr. Phillip Ransome. He is a no nonsense guy, but I like him. Our Intelligence Officer, who helps with our pre-flight briefings and leads our post battle debriefings, is Lieutenant-Colonel Herman Liebowitz. He looks like the proverbial "egg head" professor. Thinning reddish hair, slight features and eyeglasses, but "intelligence" really describes him—he is one of the brightest people I have ever met. Of course, in any group of two hundred people, there are bound to be some "stinkers". We had one in particular—he was the assistant weatherman, and he was a jerk. I know that doesn't sound very nice, but it's better than how most of the guys describe him. Here's a story about him: One day shortly after we arrived and got ourselves set up, I was going through the chow line when I was suddenly hailed from behind the food line.

"Hey, Tommy Peters! How're you doing?"

I looked and, much to my surprise, I saw Red Phillips, with whom I had attended Kingfisher High School.

104

"Red! What are you doing here?"

"Well, after we graduated I went ahead and joined the Army—it seemed like a steady job."

I laughed. "Yeah, times were tough in our neck of the woods. I see Sergeant's stripes—what are you doing back there behind the food?"

Red laughed. "When the Army found out I had worked in my folk's café since I was old enough to walk, they couldn't wait to put me in food service. I'm in charge of the chow hall here. I see you're an officer and a gentleman—and are those wings I see?"

Before I could answer, a voice behind me snarled "Lieutenant, you are an officer and officers do not chit-chat with enlisted men! You must stop this conversation at once!"

I thought he was kidding, so I smiled and explained, "This fellow and I were schoolmates back home. It's great to run into someone from my home town."

"Lieutenant, if you don't wipe that smile from your face, I'll put you up on charges for disrespecting a superior officer! Behave like an officer—do you understand?"

Good grief, I thought, *this idiot is serious!*

In my best military officer demeanor I straightened up and replied, "Yes, sir! I'm sorry, sir!"

"Then move along, and let this be lesson to you!" At that, he stomped off.

I looked at Red and him at me. We both smiled, shrugged, and went about our business. We had other conversations later, we just made sure the creep wasn't around.

THE BIG PICTURE—AND ME

There were big events happening at command levels high above ours, events that would directly affect the 336th Fighter Group. American and British leaders had long been discussing how best to carry the war forward in a decisive way, but they differed in their ideas of how. Americans believed a cross-channel invasion of the European continent was essential in defeating Nazi Germany. The British thought an approach through Italy and into the "soft underbelly" of the enemy would be more effective and less costly in lives. Allied meetings in Casablanca in January, 1943, had decided that, following success in the North Africa campaign, an invasion would be held on the island of Sicily, and then on to Anzio, in Italy, hopefully to knock Italy out of the war. At the same time, plans would be developed for a cross-channel invasion of Western Europe. At meetings in August, 1943 in Quebec, agreement was finally reached that the cross-channel invasion would be scheduled for May, 1944. That invasion had a direct impact on the 8th Air Force based in England, including effects right on down the chain of command to—ME.

It had been earlier decided to conduct the "Combined Bomber Offensive", including both English and American bomber forces, working cooperatively, to defeat Germany by reducing her ability to fight. Now that the invasion was a firm decision and a date had been set, it was necessary to revise the CBO objectives to directly support the invasion. On February 13, 1944, the issuance of a new directive defined the CBO objective as follows:

"The progressive destruction and dislocation of the German military, industrial and economic systems, the disruption of vital elements of lines of communication and the material reduction of German air combat strength, by the successful prosecution of the combined bomber offensive from all convenient bases."

Achieving air dominance over the French beaches where the invasion would have to occur was paramount. We had already been hitting the Luftwaffe whenever we could, but now it became a focus. Our task was to seek and destroy the German air force wherever we could find them.

In January, 1944, the 8th Air Force got a new commander— Lt. General Jimmy Doolittle. Yes, the same fellow who won all the pre-war air races, and the same fellow who conceived and flew the famous "Doolittle Raid" against Tokyo in April, 1942. His arrival changed the lives of us fighter pilots dramatically. With the emphasis on wiping out German air strength, General Doolittle freed us from being bound tightly to the bombers we were escorting. Instead, we were instructed to fly far ahead of the bombers' combat box formations in an "air supremacy" mode, clearing the skies of any Luftwaffe fighter opposition heading towards the target. This was a dramatic change and we "fighter boys" were ecstatic at our new freedom to be aggressively offensive rather than defensive. We soon got a chance to try the new way.

On February 19, 1944, the weather finally began to clear over central Germany. The plan was to concentrate all bombers possible on destroying the airframe and final assembly factories of Germany's single and twin-engine fighter production. We fighters would roam ahead, clearing the sky of Luftwaffe opponents. The plan became known as "Big Week".

On the early morning of February 20, after a great deal of discussion regarding the questionable weather over

England, headquarters wired the final decision: "Let 'em go!" This first attack would include over one thousand bombers, the largest strategic bombing mission we had ever mounted. There were numerous targets being hit simultaneously, and we were assigned to the groups attacking the Leipzig area.

We were up early, enjoying another of Red's "gourmet" powdered egg breakfasts. Then in for our briefing which described our new approach to escorting the bombers, and describing where we were going, the radio frequencies to be used, the route to be followed, and all the other details. We paid very close attention! Then out through the mud to our planes. I reached the "J-bird" and got ready to go with the help of my guys. We got the "start-engine" signal, and I taxied out and joined the line of fighters queued up to take off. Up successfully and quickly into the cloud cover over our base. We'd been warned about icing conditions in the clouds and I experienced a little bit, but nothing too serious. Out on top, we formed up and headed for Leipzig.

We crossed the Channel and the Netherlands but we couldn't see them because of the cloud cover. It's about 530 miles to Leipzig and, with the clouds keeping the enemy on the ground, it was a long flight. We concentrated on fuel management, using the gas in the drop tanks hanging from our wings first. Once that was gone, we would switch to our onboard tanks, using the gas in the tank behind me first. When it was empty, the airplane handled much better.

As we neared the target area, the clouds began to break up and it looked like the bombers could bomb visually rather than by radar. It also meant, however, that we could expect enemy fighters to come in great numbers. Much to my surprise, they didn't. The RAF had hit Leipzig really hard last night and apparently wore out the night fighters. We encountered a few day fighters, but we were able to keep most of them away from the bombers.

My Red Flight was on the extreme right of our squadron formation and we didn't see anyone for while. Then, suddenly, a pair of 109s came diving down on us and they scored hits on the guys in our lead flight, White Flight. I was straining my eyes to see if any others were out there, but I couldn't find any. After that abortive attack, we swung around and headed back towards the bombers. As we closed in, the sight was astounding—1000 bombers ranged in long lines through the sky! I couldn't imagine the damage they were doing to the Junkers factory that was the main target. At that moment, a radio call came through from a bomber in trouble. They'd been hit just as they dropped their load and were turning for home when a trio of enemy fighters ripped into them and knocked out an engine and injured some crew.

"White leader to Red leader, over."

I answered: "Red Leader, over."

"Red flight, detach and help that bomber. They're limping along trailing smoke ahead and to your right."

I looked and immediately located the damaged bomber in the distance, and they weren't alone. German fighters were still attacking them.

"Red Flight, follow me!"

As we closed I could see three enemy fighters taking turns attacking. They were smart, one would attack from the bomber's left, and another simultaneously from its right, and they kept trading off. It reminded me of a "run-down" in baseball.

"Red Three and Four, take the ones on the left, Red Two stay with me."

I led Jim over the bomber and down onto the fighter that was preparing to make its run. The German must have been concentrating on the bomber because he didn't seem to see us.

I lined up on him and led my fire into him. I was getting hits, but we passed too quickly to finish the job. We made a tight right turn to come back on him, but he had broken off and was trying to join his pals. Reb was dispatching one of the enemy and PJ was hitting the other, but they didn't see this third guy coming in on them. My quick judgment was that Jim and I could deal with number three without breaking Reb and PJ off their attacks.

"Jim, you're a little closer, you get that guy and I'll be right behind you!"

"Roger." Jim sounded excited.

He tightened his turn and really screamed in. I could see when he started firing and he was right on the target. The German tried to turn away, but he saw me and didn't risk it. He tried to dive, but the Mustang could drop fast and Jim stayed right on him. A lot of pieces were coming off the enemy and soon we saw smoke, then flame. The pilot bailed out and Jim had another kill. Good job, Jim!

Reb got his and so did PJ, so Red flight had a successful time. We joined up, and then closed on the injured bomber. The radio came alive:

"Thanks, Little Friends, you saved our bacon!"

"Happy to help, Big Friend," I responded. "We'll stay with you on the way out."

And we did just that. We stayed with them almost to the Channel when some P-47s came and took over. We headed for home.

Debriefing was especially interesting. Early reports stated that the bombers were very accurate on several aircraft plants in the Leipzig area and did great damage. Only 21 bombers were lost out of the 1000 that attacked. Fighter opposition was spotty, and our group claimed twelve, including the three for 501st. The first day of "Big Week" was quite successful.

The next day, February 21, was a bit different. The weather still looked good over Germany, although over England was another matter. Headquarters decided it was worth the try, so missions were scheduled. The principle target was aircraft factories at Brunswick. It is about 440 miles from our base to Brunswick, so it would be another long day.

When we got there, the weather over Brunswick was closed in and the bombers couldn't bomb visually. They tried a "pathfinder" method using radar and everyone dropped accordingly. The 501st didn't see any action.

The weather continued to look good over Germany for the 22nd, so more large formations were planned. Things did not go well.

The weather over England was awful with a thick cloud layer over 5000 feet deep. Bombers trying to take off had trouble in the clouds and several of them collided. Because of this, that portion of the attack was called off. On the way over, another large group of B-24s couldn't form up properly and were so strung out crossing the channel it was feared they'd be decimated over Germany, so they were recalled. The remainder forged on and found the clouds closed up over Oschersleben, so that group bombed other "targets of opportunity". We escorted the group going to Aschersleben (confusing names, aren't they?") and they did well visually. But the worst thing was that the Germans changed tactics.

Rather than assembling in the area of the target and trying to hit the bombers before, during, or immediately after they dropped, this time they attacked much earlier, while the bombers were still heading for their targets. That left us out in the cold and exposed the bombers to severe attacks all the way in. There were lots of reasons why they were so unprotected, but 41 out of 430 bombers attacking were destroyed. Once we learned what was happening, we fighters quickly rushed to help.

The 336th Fighter Group suffered its first losses that day. Two guys from the 500th went down, and we lost one of our "Top 10", Alan Hawkins, was last seen smoking and diving toward the ground. But the rest of us gave better than we got.

I saw a couple of FW-190s pulling up after they attacked a B-17 and I went after them with faithful Jim glued to my wing. I nailed the first one and he caught fire and I was able to drop behind the second one. He slammed into a very hard right turn and I followed him around. We were both at the edge of our plane's ability, but I was slowly tightening up on him and gaining a firing position. I finally got tight enough for a quick shot and squeezed the trigger on my control stick. To my shock, nothing happened! I kept squeezing until I could have squashed the stick, but the guns wouldn't fire. I broke out and banked away in disgust. The 190 dove away. Once I was clear, I aimed at some empty air and squeezed the trigger again. The guns fired just fine! This is weird!

At any rate, we rejoined and I quickly got a crack at a lone 190 who didn't see me coming. I lined up on him, closed to about 200 yards and squeezed again. Comfortingly, all four guns fired. I was hitting him hard and he tried to break right, like the last guy. I followed him and kept shooting. I was getting good hits as he tried to tighten his turn. I followed him until we were nearly in a high speed stall. I fired again and—nothing happened! In a tight turn, the guns would jam! Fortunately, he broke first and, as the G-forces lessened, my guns worked again and I clobbered him from his left rear quarter. Flames and smoke and down he went.

We had a very busy time for a while. It was like swatting gnats—there were Germans everywhere. I tied onto a 109 and got hits, but had to break when his buddy lined up on me. Jim got hits on him and the enemy turned and dove away. We just kept attacking everything we could see, trying to keep them off the bombers. In addition, our orders were to destroy the Luftwaffe any way we could, so we made every effort to stay on them and shoot them down. It was tense, tiring work to keep switching from target to target, and I couldn't tell when I shot one down and when I didn't. Oh, well, I just kept shooting.

Finally, the sky was clear of enemies and we all headed for home. Fuel was a concern because we'd spent so much time in dogfights, and I was almost out of ammo. I was one tired pilot when I finally settled the J-bird down onto the lovely runway at Fowlmere. Debriefing was amazing. Although the bomber losses were high, our fighters had acquitted themselves very well with a total for all of us of sixty enemy destroyed, although we lost eleven of us. I was credited with two confirmed and three probables and Jim got three probables.

Over the past three days we had made three very long flights despite very bad weather and had engaged in intense combat on two of them. It was exhausting and I was happy to drag my sorry self off to our freezing, damp hut and drop into exhausted sleep.

The next day, February 23, was forecast to have terrible weather over all of Europe, so no missions were planned and we could rest. Thank you, God! After sleeping late and skipping Red's epicurean breakfast, I got to talking with some of the other pilots and it turned out that they had experienced the same problems with their guns freezing up in high-G maneuvers. As though that weren't bad enough, there were only four guns and we all wished we had more. Finally, with the current "bird-cage" canopy, we couldn't see to our rear. That was scary because I might get shot down by somebody I couldn't see! There were rumors that a revised Mustang was coming, but that was just rumors. Oh, well, the P-51 was still a wonderful fighter and I loved my "J-bird".

The next day, February 24, saw us back in action. The weather over Germany was forecast to be good, and a major series of attacks were planned. We were covering the bombers going back to Schweinfurt to hit the ball bearing plants there. We encountered lots of action! We experienced almost all the German interceptor tricks that had been worked out against the Eighth during the previous year—coordinated attacks by four to six single-engine fighters, rockets fired at long range from twin-engine aircraft, and aerial bombs dropped from above the bomber force.

I attacked a twin-engine fighter that was firing their devilish rockets and shot him down. I then turned on 190 that was hurrying to join a couple of his friends in a frontal attack on the B-17s. I ended up in a tail-chase with him and we corkscrewed all over the sky, finally knocking off enough pieces that he flamed and went down. Much of the rest is a blur—there were enemy planes everywhere and I was shooting at anything I could get close to. It seemed like I should have shot down many more, but the pace of dog-fighting was just too fast and hectic to be able to stay with any single German long enough to bring him down. The bombers turned for home and the Nazi fighters must have run out of fuel or ammo, because they took off for home, too.

At our debriefing, we learned that our attack had been quite successful, and our force lost only eleven planes. Our fighter losses were more serious, though. Together we claimed 37 of the enemy, but we lost ten of us. One of them was a pilot from the 502nd. That was a strong reminder that our job was hazardous.

The weather on the 25th was even better over Germany, so another huge attack was planned. It would prove to be a big day for me...

We were covering the force going to Regensburg to attack the ME-109 factory there. This was a meaningful sortie for us because any way that might knock out ME-109 production would be a big help to us in the air as well. This was one time we teamed up with the Fifteenth Air Force coming up from Italy to hit common targets and it worked reasonably well. Not surprisingly, we arrived over the target area and there were swarms of enemy fighters. And as usual, the fighting was crazy and it was hard to stick with any one enemy long enough to bring him down. Nonetheless, I tucked in behind a 109, closed to about 200 yards and opened fire. I hit him, but he immediately broke left and tried to dive away. I stayed with him and got good hits and I managed to anticipate some of his evasive maneuvers, so I kept hitting him. I guess I got too fixated on shooting him down, because I suddenly started taking hits from my left rear quarter. Jim had been pulled off by another bogey, so I was on my own. I broke right and climbed, but that was only a temporary help—he latched back onto me and kept banging away. I tried everything I could think of but he stuck to me. This was my first time to be attacked so tenaciously and I didn't like it. I was throwing myself all over the sky, but this guy stayed with me and I now realized how very inexperienced I was. I was feeling his bullets hit my armor plate and I was certain I was about to die. I had heard of a trick of suddenly dropping the flaps, which would make the plane slow down suddenly, causing my pursuer to overshoot and fly past me. I tried it. It didn't work.

"Red Leader, dive straight down NOW!"

I recognized the voice of Major Stafford. I did what I was told and the violence of the pitch-over lifted me up off my seat. Then, to my right, I caught a glimpse of a red-nosed 109 with a Mustang chasing after it. Major Stafford must have seen my predicament and came to help—he saved my life!

I leveled off and turned back toward home—over 400 miles away. Stafford soon circled back and lined up on my wing.

"Red Leader, what is your status?"

I took a quick inventory of myself and my instruments.

"Red Leader is unhurt, but my engine temperature gauge is wavering."

At that moment, another Mustang came up along my other wing—faithful Jim had returned.

Major Stafford spoke again: "Red Leader, head for home. Your cooling system might be damaged, so throttle back and take it as easy as you can. Try to at least stretch it the Channel. Red Two, you accompany him."

"Roger."

I noted that we were at 23,000 feet, and I knew we were over central Germany. I set course for home, hoping to establish a slow descent that would ease the strain on my engine. In fact, I was hoping my engine was actually OK and I could just fly peacefully along. I was also greatly comforted by Jim's presence. About ten minutes later, my hopes of a trouble-free flight were dashed. The needle on my coolant gauge wasn't wavering any more—it was definitely rising. Apparently, my coolant system had been hit and was slowly leaking, allowing the engine to gradually overheat. If it got too hot, it would seize and I would no longer be flying an airplane, I would be riding a falling brick. Not good!

117

I lived up to my nickname, "Lucky", once again. As we flew across Germany, no other enemy fighters came up to knock off this cripple. Whew! Other than that, it was a long ride back toward England. We did make it to the coast, but I was down to just over 2000 feet and I was dropping faster. The temp gauge was up against the peg on the hot side, and the engine was getting rough. At least I was over the Channel, although in February, the water temperature was very cold. Not good swimming weather and I'd rather not die by freezing to death. I caught myself using body English to try to hold the airplane up—a useless endeavor, but I suppose it was a natural response.

My luck held, though, and I crossed above the England coast with hopes that I might actually reach Fowlmere. A few breathless minutes later, I was down to almost mowing the grass, but I could see the airfield in the distance. I called them on the radio.

"Gas pump, this is Raven 12 inbound with damaged coolant system. Request straight in approach."

"Raven 12, cleared for direct approach to runway zero-niner. Wind negligible."

Jim was right beside me as I moved the landing gear lever to "Down". Nothing happened. I tried twice more with the same result.

"Red Two, is my gear down?"

"Negative. No gear. And you have some red streaks running off the bottom of your belly. Looks like your hydraulics were hit, too."

"Roger." Then to the tower, "Gas Pump, Raven 12 hydraulics are out and will need to make a gear-up landing."

"Roger, Raven 12. Set down on the grass beside the runway. Crash trucks are rolling."

"Roger."

Well, as Laurel and Hardy would say, "This is a fine how-do-you-do!"

I tightened my harness, slid the canopy back and locked it, and tried to adjust my approach speed to just above a stall. I knew that when the radiator scoop hanging beneath my belly hit the ground, it would act as a great big brake and slam the plane down the rest of the way.

I was only about a hundred feet above the ground and still descending, but I should just make the field. I sure didn't want to stall at the last minute! Over the fence and above the grass, I tried to gently settle onto the grass tail first. As I felt the tail touch the ground, I pulled the throttle all the way back and flicked the master electrical switch off. Then the scoop hit and, sure enough, the plane slammed into the ground. My head was smashed into the instrument panel and my world went black.

MEMORY LANE

I had to pee. My bladder was very insistent about that, so I swung my legs over the edge of the bed and stood up.

Whoa! I'm dizzy!

I waited a moment to get my balance, and then I headed for the bathroom. The room I was in looked strange somehow, but my head wasn't working real well, so I didn't dwell on it. The next thing I noticed was that I was wearing some sort of nightgown with no back in it. Entering the bathroom, I passed a window of some sort and I caught a glimpse of some poor guy who was all banged up. He had a bandage around his head and forehead, his eyes were purple-black, and he was sort of a pasty, greenish color. I met nature's call and turned to go back to bed. As I passed the window again, I noticed that the guy I saw was moving along in the same direction I was. I thought that was strange and I paused to ponder it. Some of the fuzziness in my brain must have cleared and I was shocked to realize that it wasn't a window, it was a *mirror*!

Hmmm...

I got back in bed and soon thereafter a lady wearing a white uniform came in. It took me a minute to connect that she was a nurse.

"Did you get up out of this bed?" Asked very sternly.

"Yes. I had to go the bathroom."

"Don't you even THINK of getting out this bed again unless I'm here to help you!"

Huh?

"Uh, O.K."

"Stay there, I'll be back in few minutes."

Some of the brain fog was diminishing and I sort of figured out that I must be in a hospital.

Soon, the nurse came in and she was with a tall guy wearing a white coat. The guy looked at me for moment, and then spoke:

"Do you remember what happened to you?"

I thought hard about that, but I had no idea why I was in a hospital.

"No. sir, I don't."

The nurse spoke: "What is your name?"

I knew that one!

"Thomas Peters."

"How old are you?"

I must certainly know that one—but I just couldn't remember.

"Uh, I should know that, but I don't remember."

"Do you know where you are?"

"Well, it looks like some sort of hospital."

"In what country?"

That one stumped me.

"I have no idea. Maybe—Oklahoma?

The man in the white coat looked at the lady in the white dress.

"Nurse, I think we have a mild case of amnesia induced by the blow to his head. Continue to monitor him closely because of his concussion. I rather suspect he'll slowly regain his memory as the swelling of his brain recedes. If anything changes, call me right away."

Well, he must be doctor and I guessed right about her being a nurse.

I was told to lie still and that the nurse would be back to check on me.

I must have fallen asleep. When I awoke, my sense was that it was a different day and a different nurse appeared and began to question me. My brain seemed to have turned back on because this time, the questions were easy to answer.

"Well, welcome back Lieutenant Peters! I'm relieved that your memory has returned."

"Yes, so am I. That was really weird knowing that I should know the answers but not knowing them."

"So you're feeling better?"

"Yes. Other than a headache and my face hurts."

She smiled. "I'll bet you have a headache and, from the look of your face, it must hurt like crazy!"

I nodded.

That evening, there was noise in the hallway and a group of familiar faces peered through the door. The evening nurse was with me.

"Nurse, can we come see him?"

She thought carefully for a moment, and she looked at me very carefully. She seemed to reach a decision.

"All right, I'll let you visit three at a time for no more than five minutes. Stay quiet and don't excite him.

The first visitors were Major Stafford, Jim Weatherby, and Pappy. They filled me in on what I missed after I smashed into the instrument panel. The J-bird had lost both the coolant system and the hydraulic system. When I bellied in, the tail came down first and then the rest slammed into

122

the ground. (I vaguely remembered that part.) The plane plowed along for forty or fifty yards and then slewed to the left and stopped. Everyone was afraid of fire, so the fire trucks and crash trucks had followed right behind me. Two of the crash guys leaped onto the wing, unbuckled me, and lifted me out. Fortunately, the plane didn't burn. I was carried directly to the ambulance and it raced me to the base hospital where I was treated to stabilize my condition. Of course, I was unconscious, and the docs determined that I had a mild concussion. They decided I needed more care than they could provide, so I was transferred to a civilian hospital in Cambridge, which is where I was now.

"Well, Lieutenant," Major Stafford said, "it looks like your luck held again. We'll see you back in the air soon."

That was music to my ears! Their five minutes were up, so they left and the second group consisting of Reb, P.K., and Cowboy came in. They were hushed and obviously shocked at my appearance.

I was getting tired, but I tried to greet them cheerfully.

"Hi, fellows, it's good to see you."

They smiled shyly. Finally, Reb drawled "You look terrible, Lucky!"

I assured them that I felt about as terrible as I looked, but I was sure I'd get well soon. We chatted for another couple of minutes and then they left, too, leaving in a hail of condolences and expressions for a speedy recovery.

The next morning, I was thinking about sleep. I woke up feeling much better and I reflected on the statement that people can't really "catch up" on their sleep. I don't know about the science, but I sure felt a lot more rested. Right after breakfast—which was much better than powdered eggs and spam—the nurse came in and allowed me to get up.

"Your vital signs are stable, so it's time to get you up and about. Can you walk from here to bathroom and back?"

Since I had managed that before, I didn't expect any trouble this time. I was almost right. When I first stood up, I was a bit woozy—nothing awful, but still a little unsteady. Once I stood still for a moment I was O.K.

"Don't hurry. You're not running a race!"

After that, the trip to the bathroom and back was easy.

The nurse watched me critically. "Do you feel steady?"

"Yes. I just feel like I've been in bed too long—kind of creaky."

"Well, I want you to walk around the nursing unit. Go slowly, but right now, a bit of exercise is just what you need."

I spent the rest of the morning strolling around the nursing unit. I soon realized that I was in a room by myself, but most of the other patients were in a big room together which I learned is called a 'ward'. When I asked why I had a room, the answer was logical; "Because the ward is full and that room is all we had available. We'll be moving you out of there as soon as we can because we need it."

I had lunch in my room and I was propped up reading the newspaper when I heard a noise at the door. I looked up and there was Sarah!

"Oh, my God!" She exclaimed. She looked really horrified.

"Hi, Sarah, I'm overjoyed to see you!"

She had tears in her eyes. I suppose my beat up condition must have really affected her.

"Hey, Sarah, I'm O.K.—really! Besides, I'm posing for a new photo called 'Pilot in Technicolor'."

My terrible joke seemed to work, for she wiped her eyes and put on a smile.

"Tom, no offense, but I have never seen a face quite those colors."

I laughed. "Wait'll you see the other guy! Really, I'm doing much better. But why are you here? Did they tell you what happened? I'm thrilled to see you!"

"Well, I received a call at work from your Major Stafford and he told be you'd been injured and were in the hospital. He didn't tell me much, but he suggested a visit might do you good."

"He's quite a guy—definitely one of the Good Guys!" Here, why don't sit down and I'll tell you the story, starting with the fact that Major Stafford saved my life." Sarah looked aghast.

I went through the whole thing for her, thinking that as she came to understand what happened, she would relax. It didn't quite work.

"Tom, I am so afraid. I know as well as most people how horrible this war is, but I just didn't think—or maybe I didn't allow myself to think—about something like this happening. You're sure you're O.K?"

"Yes. The medical folks think I'll soon be fine and they can throw me out of this room because they need it. I've been walking around the ward all morning and I feel fine, my headaches are almost gone, and my memory seems to be completely back."

She took a deep breath and seemed to relax.

"Tom, you know my stance on romance with a soldier, but I have to admit that if I were ever to break my rule, you would be high on my list. Please don't get killed!"

I grinned happily. "Sarah, I am the last person who wants me to get killed and I would love to cause you to break your rule. You are a very special lady and you mean a lot to me."

She sat thoughtfully for a moment. "So what happens next?"

I assumed she meant about the Air Force. "Well, I'm not really sure. I suppose this civilian hospital will release me and I'll go back to the base. I should probably check in with our Flight Surgeon, but I don't know what they'll do next. I hope I go back on flight status."

She looked bit grim.

"Sarah, that's why I'm here, to fly and to fight. I want to stay alive as much as the next guy, especially since I have fallen in love with an incredible woman."

Her head snapped up at that and there was anger, or pain, in her eyes.

"Whoa, Sarah! I'm sorry I said that! Please don't be alarmed or angry. I'm sorry—really."

She looked deeply at me for a long time.

"Tom, let's not talk about that. We agreed on 'friends', remember?"

I nodded. "I remember."

She started to gather her things. "Well, I really do have to get back, and you know how the trains are."

"Yes," I laughed, "all those face cloths and things." Then seriously, "Sarah, I hope I didn't ruin everything—maybe my brain isn't working as well as I think it is."

She looked at me for a long moment, and then smiled. "No, Tom Peters, you haven't ruined anything. Call me when you can and tell me what happens next."

They kept me over that night, ran a series of tests the next morning, and then released me. They must have called the base because Sergeant Pistorelli showed up with a bag containing underwear, socks, my uniform, and a raincoat.

When I came to the raincoat, I looked at him questioningly.

He shrugged, "Well, Lieutenant, you know the English weather. And the weather's been lousy since you crashed."

CHANGES

Pappy had commandeered a jeep and it even had a top, which kept the rain off—sort of. We got back to the base and he dropped me off at Dr. Ransome's office. I had to wait a few minutes, but then he called me in.

"Well, Lieutenant Peters, is Humpty Dumpty back together again?"

I laughed. "I think so, sir." I handed him the large manila envelope they had given me at the hospital. He spent several minutes reading through the medical reports carefully.

"O.K.," he finally said, "a mild concussion and brief memory loss. According to them, those problems have resolved and you are back to normal functioning. It's a good thing you had your fur-lined flying helmet on—that seems to have cushioned some of the blow."

"Yes, Sir."

"Are you having any pain in your neck or back?"

"No, sir." Besides, the people at the hospital had checked that out.

"Good." He kept reading, "Pupils equal and reactive, full range of motion, coordination excellent. That's very good." He looked up at me, "As for the colorful face, that will fade in the next few days."

I was relieved to hear that.

"I want you to take it easy. I'm keeping you off flight duty for a few days and I want you to report to me every morning. Don't look so alarmed, the weather is atrocious and no one is flying anyway."

He wrote something a slip of paper and handed it to me.

"Take this to Major Stafford. Besides, I think he wants to see you anyway."

So off I went, trudging through the rain in my already soaked raincoat.

When I knocked on his door, Major Stafford called "Come!"

I marched in and reported just like they taught us back in training.

He smiled and said "At Ease. Sit down, Lucky, I want to talk to you."

Uh, oh, I thought, *this sounds serious!*

I handed him the slip from Doc Ransome. He glanced at it and said, "No problem, nobody's going anywhere in this soup anyway. The weather's so bad not even the ducks are flying."

I smiled at the time-worn old joke.

"O.K., a couple of things. First, so long as the medicos release you, you'll be back on full flying status, so don't be worried about that."

I really smiled at that!

"Second, how did you manage to hit your head? Wasn't your harness tight?"

I tried to remember back. I clearly remembered tightening my harness and locking the canopy open. I told that to Major Stafford.

"That's strange, it should have held you back. I'll have someone look at the wreck and see if something broke. Or maybe we have a problem we don't know we have."

He paused and looked seriously at me. "My third item is the most important. It concerns how you came to be damaged in the first place. Tell me about the dogfight."

Hmm. It almost sounds like I did something wrong.

I quickly got my thoughts in order and then told him what had happened. I had locked onto the tail of the 109 and as we twisted and turned, I was staying with him and getting hits. All of a sudden, I started taking hits from my left rear quarter. I explained how I had tried every maneuver I knew, but nothing worked to shake my attacker. It was only when he, Major Stafford, came to the rescue that I got loose. He listened intently to my every word.

"How long were you behind the 109?"

I thought about that. "Probably about 25 or 30 seconds. We twisted a lot."

Stafford nodded. "What do you think about that?"

I knew what he meant. "Sir, I stayed on him too long without looking around."

He nodded. "That's right, Lucky. I keep telling you guys to keep your head on a swivel, even when you're attacking. The other guy caught you napping and nailed you."

He paused. "Now for my big question: what maneuvers did you try? What did you do to evade him?"

I replayed the fight in my head and described with words and hand motions what I'd done. When I finished, Stafford nodded grimly.

"That's what I was afraid of. You did everything in the book. That's the problem—'In the Book'."

I must have looked puzzled.

"Peters, you were beat by your inexperience. You did every maneuver you have been taught. The trouble is, in the real world, that isn't enough. Over Germany, with a good enemy pilot latched on behind you, you need MORE than the book. You have to move into the realm of what you sense, what you feel, what you know, not just what you were taught. Simply put, you need to INVENT moves that fit the situation. Do you understand what I'm saying?"

I thought about his words and suddenly I knew what he meant.

"Yes, Major Stafford, I clearly understand what you mean. In fact, it just occurred to me that I'm still thinking like a student pilot. I'm afraid to try anything different because I might hurt the airplane. I'm afraid I'll get in trouble."

He beamed. "Exactly! And you WILL get in trouble—not with me or the Army—but you can lose your life. Throw caution to the wind—it's time to invent some moves of your own!"

Wow! That was probably the best advice I'd ever heard!

"Actually, Tom, you've given me the idea that we need a pilot's meeting. You are certainly not the only one in this position."

And we did have a pilot's meeting, the next morning at 0900. The entire group was there with all three squadron leaders talking to us about innovative moves. It was fascinating!

It wasn't just a lecture, it was both that and an open forum. We could ask whatever we wanted. The squadron leaders shared their experience and some tricks they'd learned, things like slipping the airplane to get an attacker to overshoot, and even various ways to use a stall to good advantage. We talked all morning and the excitement was palpable. It was a bunch of inspired, energized fighter pilots who walked out of the room when the meeting ended. We kept on talking and inventing among ourselves back at the hut. Wow!

It was March 3 when I got out of the hospital. On March 4, something momentous happened. The 336th was

131

grounded by weather, but while we were having our meeting, in spite of the weather, Eighth Air Force managed to get an attack through all the way to Berlin! The first Berlin mission! It didn't knock down much, but the effect on morale was electric. We had reached Berlin, and we would keep going back!

I kept checking in with Doc Ransome for another five days and I didn't do any flying. But the weather, as usual, was terrible, although they did manage a couple more missions to Berlin and the 336th took part. On March 6, a big group hit the German capital, especially focused on some factories there. The enemy responded vigorously and the 8th lost eleven fighters and sixty-nine bombers. American fighters claimed eighty-two enemy planes destroyed, though. Thankfully, everyone from the 336th came through O.K.

March 8 was another big day. First, Doc released me to flying status, although too late to join the mission that day. The other was the mission. For the first time, the weather was clear over Berlin and our huge force really walloped them. Apparently, too, the sight of hundreds of American heavy bombers, flying in perfect formation over their capital city, really upset the German populace. Eighth Air Force lost seventeen fighters, but we claimed eighty-seven enemy downed. Again, all 336th guys came home safe. Interestingly, they reported that the German fighter opposition seemed weaker than the mission on the 6th, although, obviously, they were still very dangerous.

After that, the weather really closed in and we were told we wouldn't be flying for a few days. Major Stafford gave groups of us "local Leave" of three days, which would allow us to go no farther than Cambridge. I was in the first group and I managed to call Sarah and report that. Her response startled me.

"Lieutenant Peters, you are clearly still in need of close observation. I will, therefore, take a couple of days off and meet you in Cambridge. There's a pub downtown called 'The Swan". I'll meet you there as soon as I can catch a train."

I think my heart stopped.

"A WOMAN'S PREROGATIVE..."

I had called Sarah at about 0930. I made it to the Swan by about 11:00. Much to my surprise, the pub door opened at 12:15 and all the sunshine in the world stood in the doorway. There must not have been any crucial face cloth deliveries that morning! I left my bar stool and went to greet her.

"Hi."

She smiled. "Hello".

The moment was decidedly awkward. I was thrilled to see her, but I just couldn't accept what I thought was the meaning of her telephone message. I didn't want to presume and, as a result, I didn't really know what to do. My unease was obvious.

Sarah smiled a bit abashedly and, as the silence became embarrassing, she spoke:

"Tom, let's go get a room. There is a small guest house not far from here where student families often stay during university events.

A room was available and the check-in was simple. We found our room—I will always remember 104—and we entered and put our stuff down. There was a single bed. I turned to her...

"Uh, Sarah...?"

There was a pause before she answered.

"Tom," she sounded nervous, "I know this must be confusing for you. Actually, it's confusing for me, too."

I suppose by that point my perplexity could have been cut with a knife and I'm sure my face showed it.

She continued. "When I saw you in that hospital bed, all banged up and bruised in all those ghastly colors, I suddenly realized something important—something I hadn't allowed myself to think about."

I waited.

"I know I have stated, rather firmly, that I don't want to get involved with someone who might be killed in the war. But I know, as well as anyone, that *anyone* can be killed in this war. Seeing you there in the hospital shocked me into realizing that I can't just put my life on hold until the war ends. People all around me have learned to live for the moment, for there might not be a tomorrow. You have become very special to me and I don't want to miss the opportunity of time together."

I was breathless, but Sarah misinterpreted my silence.

"Well. Tom, if you think I'm some sort of cheap person or something, I'll leave right now." She bent to pick up her bag.

"Sarah, no!" The thought of her walking out that door was unbearable.

I went to her and grabbed her into my arms and held her tight. She began sobbing into my shoulder.

"Sarah, you are the finest woman I have ever met and you couldn't be 'cheap' if you tried! If you walk out that door, I'll be a war casualty right here in this room! In the hospital, I slipped and told you I was falling in love with you. You may not be ready to hear that, but it's true."

She straightened and wiped her eyes.

135

"Well, sir, you know what they say—it's a woman's prerogative to change her mind. And here we are. Let's make the most of it!"

And so we did. I won't tell you *all* of it, but I will share some of it.

We found a delightful form of exploration and discovery without leaving our room. The cold rain outside was as if the sun were shining brightly.

That evening, we dodged raindrops and found a cozy café Sarah knew from her times in Cambridge with John. The food wasn't great, though it was better than Red's runny powdered eggs, but we talked and laughed and laughed and talked. I was happier than I have ever been.

The next afternoon, we did something I would never have considered—we went to a lecture! That's right, a lecture! We were at one of the greatest universities in the world and the intellectual opportunities were amazing. We attended a talk entitled "The Englishman at War", presented by a Don of the history department. It was a fascinating discourse on how the English tend to comport themselves when at war. For this Yank from the wilds of Oklahoma, it was a very interesting talk and I gained a much deeper understanding of how the English managed to remain so stalwart even when the sky was raining bombs and the world was literally crashing down around them. It explained some of the strengths I saw in Sarah and helped me to form an even more inspired view of these wonderful people and this wonderful girl.

That evening, we tried attending movie, a classic propaganda-filled excitement about the brave fighter pilots and their daring exploits. By the time we'd been in there a half hour, I was squirming. Sarah looked over at me with a quizzical expression.

"Tom?" She whispered.

At that moment, the film showed the intrepid birdman throwing his controls around as if he were churning milk and I couldn't contain myself any longer and I burst out in a laugh. I tried to smother it, but the people around me heard. It was very embarrassing.

"Sarah," I whispered, "I'm sorry! But can we leave? This nonsense is more than I can take!"

And leave we did, to the accompaniment of a few dirty looks.

Our time together came to a much too rapid close, but there were two things that will always remain in my memory. One of them you can imagine, but the other regards the time we spent talking. Yes, talking. We discussed everything under the sun and as we did, I came to appreciate not only Sarah's profound intelligence, and not only *what* she thinks, but also *how* she thinks; the way she processes information and draws conclusions. And I came to learn the essential things about her—what she values, what are the 'non-negotiables' to her, the things that make her smile, and the things that make her sad. The depth of Sarah Brockman was breathtaking, and I came to know I was totally in love with her.

As we gathered our things in order to leave, I shared that with her. I knew it was a risk, but I felt it was important and I wanted her to know that my feelings were serious and not just some casual fling.

She listened carefully and I couldn't read her expression.

"Sarah, I'm sorry if I'm getting more serious than you want. But I want you to know how deeply I respect you and how deeply I admire you. I am serious when I say 'I love you.'"

After a pause, she responded.

"Thomas Peters, you slay me! One of the many things about you that attract me is your gentlemanliness." She chuckled, "Maybe that's not really a word, but I'll use it anyway."

She continued, "I know that you are a very honorable man; that you are very respectful, considerate, and kind—and not just with me. I see those qualities in how you treat everyone. The better I know you, the more I admire you. You say you love me, and I believe you. I accept your love with deep emotion. I am still trying to overcome my fear of loving and losing—again. I am very close to repeating your declaration back to you. Give me just a bit more time, Tom, and I pray I will soon say those magic three words to you. Can you accept that?"

My heart was bursting and my eyes were wet.

"Sarah, I will wait until the end of time if it means I might win your heart and your love!"

We almost crashed into a long embrace.

"Sarah, you are the greatest inspiration in my life, the inspiration to survive this awful war. I'll fight with everything I have within me to help bring it to an end. I'll stay alive, Sarah, I'll stay alive because I love you!"

Our parting the Cambridge main rail station was heart-wrenching, but now I had a reason to live!

SHINY THINGS

I don't know how he did it, but Pappy showed up again at just the right time. I don't know if he just followed me around, or if he simply had a great sense of timing, but here he was again. Sarah's train had just pulled out and, as I exited the station building, I heard a "shave-and-haircut" beep on a jeep's horn and up to the curb pulled Pappy.

"Pappy, how do you it? You always show up just when I need a ride back to base."

All I got was an enigmatic smile.

"Pappy, you'd be a good model for the Mona Lisa. Oh, well, I'm happy to see you."

"Lieutenant, you don't look especially happy but, under the circumstances, I wouldn't expect you to. Have a good leave?"

I just nodded. He pulled out into the slow-moving traffic and headed for Fowlmere. As we got going I noticed the smile hadn't left his face.

"Pappy, what are you smiling at now? You look positively gleeful."

He just glanced at me, still wearing that mysterious smile, and said nothing. In fact, the usually loquacious Pappy said nothing on the entire drive back. I was still lost in thoughts of Sarah, but I wasn't so far gone that I couldn't help but notice his unusual silence and the strange smile. Finally, as we neared the base and in an effort to start a conversation, I asked him a simple question:

"So, how are things at the 501st? Anything exciting happen while I was gone?"

He smiled even more.

I was really flummoxed now. "Pappy? What's going on?"

As we entered the base, some of the ever-present clouds thinned a bit and we got some random rays of the milky English March sunshine. Pappy surprised me when he didn't turn off to the officer's huts, but kept going towards the flight line.

"Come on, Pappy, what's up? I feel like I'm being kidnapped."

As we passed between the hangers we approached the usual line of fighters. But there was something wrong. The planes didn't look right but I couldn't immediately tell what the problem was. As we pulled near them I was suddenly overcome by shock and astonishment.

"Lieutenant, while you were away, we received your replacement airplane for the one you wrecked. Here's the new J-bird..."

It was as though a stage manager timed it perfectly. A beam of late afternoon sunlight shone on the brilliant silver airplane in front of me. It was a P-51—but it *wasn't* a P-51. At least, not like the olive drab airplane I was used to. This one was silver, and the lines were different. That's when it hit me, the cockpit was different. Instead of the birdcage I was used to, this one had a sort of clear dome or bubble on top. Len Watkins and Larry Priestman were there with huge smiles, which got even bigger at my astonishment.

"Lieutenant, welcome to your new P-51...*D* model!"

The best description I can give is that I was looking at a work of art. The earlier Mustangs were sleek machines, but this took the award for beauty. The flow of sleek lines from the prop hub, over the hood, past the new bubble top to the rear of the fuselage was stunning. The fin leading to the rudder had an added extension that made the entire top of the airplane just one flowing line.

"Lieutenant, notice the wings..."

I walked over to the left wing. "Guys, it's shaped different, and it's a little thicker..."

Len, my Armorer, gestured to the leading edge.

"Holy Cow! Three guns! Does it really have six?!"

"Yes sir! And they sit right-side-up, so they won't jam like your old ones."

"What happened? Where did this come from? Is mine the only one?"

Pappy grinned. "No, sir. You were due for a replacement, but the Group awarded the first few new ones to us. The entire 501st got new ones and our old ones went back to the depot for rebuilding as replacements. These arrived the day after you left."

Pappy walked over and handed me a pilot's manual. "Looks like you have some homework, Lieutenant."

It turned out that nearly all the procedures in the book were the same as before because the engine was the same wonderful Merlin. The spotty weather gave us a chance to test fly our new fighters and to become oriented to them. The biggest difference was that we could SEE! We could swivel our heads and see all around us! Hooray! We of Red Flight spent many excited hours "hanger flying" our new steeds and we loved them. We were also eager to get back to the war—our general ambition was to fight the war and get it over with as soon as possible. And, yes, I certainly had Sarah in mind!

Meanwhile, the war continued. Our efforts during "Big Week" were judged very successful, but our leaders were feeling the pressure of the upcoming invasion code-named

"Overlord". Our AAF leaders felt it was vital to the success of the invasion that we hold air superiority over the invasion area, so our focus was described by General Arnold as "destroy the German Air Force in the air, on the ground, in the factories..."

We went back to war on March 22. We headed towards Berlin to attack the Heinkel plant at Oranienburg and the FW-190 engine plant at Basdorf. It was a long ride in the usual bad weather and the Luftwaffe did not respond in any strength. I saw a couple of ME-110s at a distance, but they were too far away for Red Flight to attack. It was an even longer ride home.

By the end of March, though, we sensed something important. It became apparent during this month that the German Air Force had lost the advantage it had maintained so successfully from the fall of 1943 to late February, 1944. We noted that when escorting fighters were present, the Germans showed a marked disinclination to tangle either with the bombers or with the escort. It seemed we were gaining the upper hand, but when the enemy chose not to come up and play, it made it harder for us to achieve our purpose of destroying them altogether. April would turn out to be a pivotal month.

By April 1, the plan was for the invasion to take place around May 1. Although the huge air battles of late 1943 and early 1944 had wreaked havoc with the Luftwaffe, there were other vital needs preparatory to the invasion, including as total as possible a disruption of the German and French transport networks, especially the railways. After a great deal of contention in our leadership circles, it was decided to shift the focus of the 8th Air Force from strategic bombing of German factories to the destruction of the European rail and transportation network. But it was emphasized that wherever we went, the goal of the fighters was to force the German air force into battle to defend their homeland so we could destroy the enemy's air power before the big invasion.

APRIL

On April 1, we joined up with over 400 B-17s and B-24s for a mission to Ludwigshafen but everything got messed up. The weather was impossible, the B-17s turned back and the B-24s ended up scattered all over Europe. Total fighter claims were 18 destroyed for the loss of four of ours. Overall, not one of our better days.

One interesting bit of news: on April 4 we got neighbors! The 339th Fighter Squadron arrived at Fowlmere. Welcome home, Guys!

On April 5, we did something new for the 501st—come along and I'll explain.

We were up, fed, briefed and to the airplanes by 0630. Our assignment was a new one for us—to attack Luftwaffe airfields across Germany. Us—the fighters—NOT the bombers.

Pappy reported that the J-bird was fueled, fully armed, and in great shape. I did a quick walk-around and then climbed in. Pappy helped me don my parachute, fasten my harness, and get settled as comfortably as possible.

First, I check my controls and assure that the rudder, ailerons, and elevator operate fully and smoothly. Then, starting from my left and working clockwise around the cockpit, I first make sure the flap handle is all the way up in the "up" position. Next, I move the carburetor warm air control to the forward "normal" position and the carburetor cold air control to the forward "ram air" position. Next, I set the coolant and oil radiator air control switches to the "auto" position. Now I adjust the trim tabs for takeoff—rudder trim set to 5 degrees right, elevator trim to 4 degrees nose down (this compensates for the weight of the fuel in the fuselage tank right behind my seat), and aileron trim to "neutral". On the throttle quadrant, I set the propeller rpm control all the way forward to "increase" and the mixture control is set forward to "idle cutoff". The throttle handle is set to about one inch forward from the rearmost position. Now I go to the engine controls on and around the front dash, starting with the fuel booster pump switch, which I set in the up "on" position. Then I set the ignition switch to "both" to utilize both magnetos. Beneath the panel, just forward of the control stick, I set the fuel tank selector to the "main tank-LH" position and I flip the fuel shutoff valve to the "on" position. I also make sure the parking brake is set. On the right side of the cockpit are the electrical control panels. I set the battery switch in the "up" position to supply electrical power and I flip the generator switch to the up "on" position. Now I move back to the front panel and click and hold the primer switch for a second or two to get some fuel into the engine. Now I can finally start the engine. After checking with Pappy to make sure no one is near the propeller, I press and hold the starter switch which starts the engine turning. When the engine begins to "catch" or try to fire, I move the fuel mixture control lever on the throttle quadrant to the "run" position. When the engine starts, I adjust the throttle to about 1200 RPM and I monitor the oil pressure gauge to be sure it reaches at least 50 psi and the engine temperature gauge reaches a temperature of about 100 degrees F. The vacuum gauge should show between 3.75 and 4.25 inches and the hydraulic pressure gauge should read 800 to 1100 psi. The oxygen pressure gauge should read 400 psi. When all is well, and I get the signal to taxi, I make sure the tail wheel is unlocked, I release the parking brake and advance the throttle slightly to begin taxiing.

Not exactly like jumping into your Ford and turning the key, is it? I described all of this so you can begin to understand why our training was so lengthy and detailed.

I get in line and taxi out. I am constantly amazed at how many P-51s make up the 336th Fighter Group. Seeing a line of 48 shining P-51D airplanes ready to take off is breathtaking. And we are just one group! Anyway, off we go.

On April 5, we climbed out, formed up, and set off on the long ride to Germany. We went to western Germany and then Major Stafford led us down to attack the first airfield we encountered. It had a few fighters scattered along the tarmac and we dove in for low-level strafing attacks. White flight went first; then I led Red flight down for our turn.

I must comment on strafing an enemy airfield: although it sounds like a fun and exciting endeavor, the reality is anything but fun. It IS exciting, but NOT fun! You see, the enemy rings his airfields with antiaircraft guns and their entire goal is to blow a low-flying Mustang or Thunderbolt or Spitfire out of existence. If you are able to sneak up on them, the first few strafing planes can get in and out before the gunners get ready. Anyone coming later, however, faces a prepared and deadly enemy. They were ready for Red flight.

As I dove in and made my pass, several of the parked planes were already smoking or burning. I tried to fire at the ones that still appeared to be O.K. I was moving fast and I was very low, so I only had a second or so to aim and fire. I walked my gunfire into one FW-190 with a yellow tail, and then into the next one right beside him. Then I pulled hard to jump over a building and get out of there. I could see the muzzle smoke from the AA guns tracking me as I passed. Jim and I were lucky (there's that nickname again!), but Reb and PK weren't. As we climbed out, Major Stafford radioed to end the attack and reform. Reb reported he had taken hits and wasn't sure about his damage. PK reported he had damage and his engine was failing fast , so Major Stafford ordered them to cover each

146

other to head for home. Suddenly, my Red flight was cut in half. Jim and I attached ourselves to White flight and off we went, looking for another airfield that was supposed to be located a few miles north. We quickly found it but saw only a single tri-motored transport that looked like it had already burned, so we moved on.

We attacked two more fields that day, one had a variety of old-looking planes, and the other had a respectable collection of about a dozen ME-110s. In both cases, Major Stafford just sent in one flight to make a quick hit-and-run attack. I was in on the one for the ME-110s and we pretty well wiped them out. As always, though, the ground fire was ferocious.

As we headed for home, two or three of us still had a bit of ammo—and it was a good thing. As were passing in the vicinity of Amiens, France, we were jumped by about a dozen ME-109s. They dove on us and caught us napping. One of the guys from Blue flight saw them at the last minute and called "Break"! We scattered, but I knew I was one of the few with ammunition, so I did a tight, climbing turn and went after a 109 that latched onto one of our guys. I came in fast and made a curving pass and was able to lead him well. He flew into my stream and immediately started smoking. The canopy flew off and the pilot bailed out. That carried me around and onto the tail of another. And, yes, my head was swiveling constantly! I love our new bubble canopy!

I slid in behind him and closed to about 150 yards and opened fire. I kicked my rudder slightly back and forth (we called it "sawing the rudder") and my six fifties really chewed him up. Suddenly his nose veered up and then he fell off into a spin that ended when he hit the ground. I banked back toward the action, but it seemed to be over. We three with ammo had accounted for five of the twelve that had attacked us. I guess that scared off the rest, but if they'd known how defenseless we were then, they'd have wiped us out. Lucky, again?

When we got back, we learned that Reb had made it back across the Channel and had crash landed at a British airfield near the coast. The word was he was shaken up and bruised, but O.K. Sadly, PK's engine lasted just long enough for him to bail out over France—Nazi occupied France. Very sad! My every wish is that he'll make it out alive!

Our first foray into the joys of low-level strafing had taught us many lessons. One was that my old friend, the P-47 Thunderbolt, was vastly better suited for low level attacking. It was rugged, and the air-cooled radial engine wasn't as susceptible to ground fire as was our liquid-cooled Merlin with its radiator and all its plumbing.

On April 8, we went again, but this time as escorts for 330 B-24 bombers going to Brunswick. It was a bizarre experience.

I was still down two planes from Red flight, so Jim and I attached ourselves to Stafford's White flight again. We took off, got into position and headed east; over Germany, we were slightly ahead of the bombers. Over Lingen, Dummer Lake, Steinhuder Lake, and Hanover, we met no enemy opposition at all. Even as we crossed Brunswick itself—no opposition. It looked like another no-show for the enemy fighters and I suppose we started to relax. But then, about 40 miles northeast of Brunswick, we suddenly encountered a large concentration of about 150 enemy fighters. What was surprising was that a group of B-24s were already there! It turned out that they made a navigational error and "cut the corner" of the planned approach path and arrived even before we fighters did. Once we got there, we tore into the fighters and fierce combat ensued. I went after a 109 and made quick hits and down he went. I then latched onto the tail of another and was getting good hits when he smoked and turned away. Still with faithful Jim at my side, we turned into a head-on attack of two 190s. Who would blink first? They did—Jim got a confirmed and I got a probable. It was insane—there were airplanes everywhere, zooming, diving, climbing, turning—I couldn't turn my head fast enough to keep up with it all. When it finally ended, the tally was gruesome; that group of B-24s lost 30 planes! The entire force lost 34 bombers and we lost 22 fighters. Our Blue flight lost one and Yellow lost one. Not a good day.

April 10, 1944—another hard day of work. Two things were happening at once: the weather was getting slightly better, and the preparations for the big invasion were really heating up. This time, more than 650 bombers set out to hit the Luftwaffe hard, including factories, airfields and as many fighters as we could entice to up and tangle with us. We covered a group of B-17s attacking aircraft repair facilities in Brussels, Belgium, and it looked to me like they really plastered the target. Enemy fighter opposition was very weak and it seemed like the Germans weren't willing to risk their fighters to protect targets in northwestern Europe. Only one B-17 was lost and only one P-51 from the Ninth Air Force. The guys from the Ninth had good success in other places that day, claiming 40 enemy fighters downed.

April 11 was noteworthy—in a bad way. Nearly 1000 bombers and more than 800 fighters, including 250 P-51s, set out for northern Germany with plans to attack several aviation-related targets. The Germans got serious this time. We escorted 300 of the B-17s for attacks on Rostock, Politz, and Arnimswald. Enemy fighters were waiting and ready, and they sent in everything that would fly—single engine, twin-engine, everything. They fired rockets, dropped bombs on the B-17s, and made very determined machinegun and cannon attacks. We tangled with them continuously from the time we approached the target until well after we headed for home.

My excitement started with an ME-110 attacking me from my right. I guess he expected me to roll left and dive—but I didn't. I chopped my throttle for an instant, which slowed me suddenly. That made his fire pass ahead of me. At the same time, as I powered up again, I dove to the right, which made him pass over me so I could zoom back up behind him. It worked—and I got him! As I turned away to find another target Jim called "Break Left!" I did and the bullets from a FW-190 that would have hit my engine— and maybe me—instead punched a few holes in my right wing. Jim swung in on the 190 and got him. The German fighters were focusing on the bombers, of course, but there were so many of them we couldn't stop them all. But we tried!

It was a confused swirl of airplanes spitting death and I slammed the J-bird around so hard I thought I'd tear the wings off. I was shooting at anything that didn't have a star on its side, simply trying to scare them away from the bombers. But they were determined and they were terribly successful. I managed to hit lots of other targets, but I couldn't keep track of who went down and who didn't. When it finally ended, the score was horrendous.

At briefing when we got back we learned the final toll. From our group of 300 bombers, 33 were lost! And it gets worse—total bomber losses for the day were 64 lost—one of the heaviest single-day losses in the entire war. And it wasn't just the bombers—

That day, twenty-three fighters were lost, including nine P-51s. In that nine were three from the 336th: Roger Adams of Blue Flight went down over Germany under the guns of a FW-190; Pete Davis of White flight was last seen descending with smoke trailing; and Bill Allen from Yellow Flight didn't show up back at Fowlmere. Our Quonset hut was lost in depression that night.

I woke up on the morning of the twelfth with a toothache. How ridiculous! But it was really painful and I knew flying would make it hurt much worse. I told Major Stafford and he sent me to the base dentist, and Jim flew with Stafford that day. The dentist told me I had a root infection and he wanted to try using Penicillin, which I approved. That took me off flying for the next week. The day wasn't all bad, though—Reb returned and was pronounced ready to fly. I was thrilled to see him, but we were both saddened by the recent losses in the 501st. It also turned out that the guys who went to Germany came back empty-handed because the weather closed in and they had to abort.

It was time to reconstitute Red Flight. Now that Reb was back, he would move to the Red Three position, so I only needed one pilot and Major Stafford gave me Will Jamison—the raucous "Rustler"—to fly as Red Four. There was more shuffling and soon the 501st was back to full strength, including a couple of replacement pilots fresh from the States.

During the time I was off, a mission of note occurred on April 15. Over 600 fighters were sent out on strafing sweeps of Western and Central Germany. From among the total, 222 P-51s claimed 30 German aircraft destroyed but 15 P-51s were lost. Strafing is a hazardous business!

On April 19, I was back in the saddle and we escorted B-17s to the Kassel area. I shot at several enemy fighters but couldn't make any claims. I flew a couple of missions over the next few days, but nothing noteworthy happened. Finally, on April 24, we took part in a significantly successful mission.

We again accompanied B-17s to Friedrichshafen and we encountered significant opposition. I attacked an ME-410 and shot him down. Jim took the lead on a ME-109 and got him and then I led us to a group of FW-190s. I latched onto one and stuck with him through some fancy aerobatics (while always keeping my swiveling!) and finally got him. I hit a couple of others, but I couldn't hang around long enough to determine if they were probables or just damaged. Then life got scary. A 190 snuck up behind and below me while Jim was off after one of the 190s and suddenly, I'm being jolted by machine gun and cannon fire. The machine gun hits sounded like hail hitting a tin roof, but the cannon shells shook the whole airplane. I tried to dive and turn away, but he stayed with me. I tried a barrel roll, but that didn't work, and then I remembered Jim Stafford's advice.

I played a little basketball in high school and I remembered the value of a "head fake" in confusing a defender. I decided to try a P-51 version of a "head fake". I slammed the stick hard left just for an instant. The plane started to snap into a left aileron roll and the German started to follow. I then slammed the stick all the way over to the right and hauled hard to turn sharply away. It worked. He hesitated just long enough for me to continue to dive and turn behind and beneath him. Just as I began to pull onto his tail, I noticed machinegun fire hitting him from above and behind. It was Reb to the rescue and he got the 190! Thank you, Reb! Moments later, Jim was back and Rustler joined up, too, so Red Flight was together and on the prowl. I assessed my plane for damage and everything important seemed O.K., so we joined back in the melee and Reb and Rustler each got another 109 apiece. The final tally for that day for just   P-51s was 64 confirmed and the 336th claimed eleven. Although twelve P-51s were lost, the 336th all came through safely. Pappy remonstrated with me about all the holes in my shiny new J-bird...

The 501st sat out the next three days' missions so our airplanes could be put back in shape.

On April 28, we escorted a group of B-17s to hit some rail yards in France. It was a short, quick mission, but no fighter action for us. On the 29th, we went to Berlin—not a short, quick mission! The bombers were concentrating on railway facilities in Berlin and the fighters came up. Over 800 American fighters took part. The 501st got seven, but I made no claims. Total fighter claims for the mission were 95 enemy fighters destroyed.

On April 30, we escorted bombers to attack more French railway installations. It was an empty day for 501st.

And thus ended one of the busiest months in our fighter operations. Our brothers in the Ninth Air Force had become masters of low altitude attacks and strafing. We were competent professionals in long-range escort. We sent out thousands of bombers and it seemed that Germany simply could not survive—but they just wouldn't quit. By this time, it had been decided that the invasion would take place in late May or early June and the time before then would be focused on assuring that the landings would not be interrupted by German aviation and that the enemy's ability to move troops and equipment into the invasion area would disrupted as completely as possible. We were in the thick of it.

THE MERRY MONTH OF MAY

Events had settled into something of a pattern: the Ninth Air Force guys focused on attacks all across France, while we Eighth Air force guys continued to escort the bombers into Germany. But there was a difference for us—we were not only allowed, but we were ORDERED to make ground attacks against airfields and even trains in western Germany and eastern France. I mention the trains specifically because until then, we had been cautious about possible civilian casualties in train attacks, but now Headquarters decided that civilians weren't using the trains much because it was too dangerous so we could— and should—attack them, but especially freight trains. In connection with that, I met with my Red Flight fellows and we devised our strategy for attacking rail targets. I'll mention some experiences in that vein in a moment, but now I want to stress how hectic and tiring our month of May turned out to be. April had already worn us out and now in May we flew and flew and flew. Our airplanes stared to wear out and we pilots wore out even more. Events became an exhausted blur.

May started off with decent weather and we continued flying escort and doing low level strafing. I'll skip those details but highlight the railway adventures.

So—a couple of "train-busting" stories: On May 9, we were on our way back from bombing rail yards in Belgium and we went train hunting. Somewhere near the French border, I sighted a plume of smoke moving across the horizon. We were still at about 5000 feet altitude so it was soon obvious that a freight train was heading into France—a perfect target! I led Red Flight around and we split up. Jim and I would attack the front of the train from the east, and Reb and Rustler would attack the back part from the west. Since I was on the left, I would attack the engine, and Jim would attack the first few cars behind the engine.

We dropped down and raced in. You will recall my earlier comments regarding strafing airfields and how they were ringed with anti-aircraft guns—well, the train wasn't, it was all by itself and just passing into a large meadow area. This time, our attack WAS fun; we approached low and fast and started firing from a comfortable distance away. I poured my six fifty-caliber guns right into the locomotive. Just as I was about to pull up, the boiler exploded into a towering geyser of steam. That train won't be going anywhere for a while! Up and over and away. About a mile out, I turned and headed back, Jim right off my right wing. Reb and Rustler had done well—there were burning freight cars toward the rear of the train. We got a good sight of each other so we wouldn't collide and then went back for one more pass. Lots of gunfire and lots of debris flying off the train. Soon, more fires. Good enough for "Train Number One"!

Over the next several missions, we got lots of practice in "train-busting" and it was actually fun tearing up freight trains. I was still a little uncomfortable attacking passenger trains, but the other guys commented that since civilians weren't riding the trains, German soldiers were.

Yeah, I guess... I thought.

The Germans were smart, though. We found out how smart on May 19 when we escorted the bombers to Berlin. We had a hot time with enemy fighters, but there were so many American fighters that we hadn't used all our ammo, so we went train-chasing again.

We found an unusually long freight train just inside the French border. I claimed the train for Red Flight and in we went. As we approached, I noticed that the third freight car back carried a really large wooden crate, but I didn't think much about it.

This time it was Jim's turn to take the engine, so I decided I'd focus on the large crate. Low and fast, the ground skimming beneath us in a blur, we approached and started firing. Much to my astonishment, the "large crate" suddenly dropped its sides and an anti-aircraft gun started blazing away at me! They had mounted a gun and hidden it in a false crate—smart! I quickly zoomed up and they couldn't track me fast enough, but if passed over to the other side, I'd be an easy target. As I zoomed above them I cranked into a really hard turn to the left thinking that if I flew along low above the train, the train cars would shield me from the gun. It sort of worked. The gun at the front didn't track me, but there was another one in the middle and a third one at the end. I ended up diving low and jinking away—boy was I puckered up!

I reformed Red Flight and it turned out everyone was OK. I also remembered back to my Oklahoma upbringing and hearing the stories of the way the Indians attacked a wagon train. I wasn't about to let that train get away; it was obviously important enough to protect, and it was unusually long. So the plan was as follows: one of us would attack a gun head-on, hopefully drawing their concentration, and one of the others would come in behind the gun and destroy it. Obviously, we had to be extremely careful not to shoot each other or collide. The other big problem was there are three guns and four P-51s—our plan could account for two of the guns but the third one was free to nail us. Our only hope was fly fast and low and shoot straight!

On the radio: "Red Two, you come from behind them and as you get close, break to your right, and I'll break to my right also."

"Roger."

So in we went. I was head-on into a duel with gun. I opened fire a bit far out, hoping maybe they'd duck. They didn't. Their fire was swinging in on me as they got a bead on me and I was hitting all around them. I got a glimpse of Jim on the other side and we were closing fast. Between his fire and mine, the gun went silent just before we broke away.

Jim also took an opportunity when he saw it. As he turned away, it brought him into a firing position on the center gun. I had turned away from the train and I had circled back when I noted the gunners from the center gun dropping off the railcar and running for cover. Jim's fire, combined with the destruction of both of their mates, seemed to convince them that their days were numbered, so they took off.

We used up the rest of our ammo and did some good damage, but it was a long train and still needed more working over, so I called our Controller and reported the train. She said they'd send an attack as soon as possible. I later heard they sent some Ninth Air Force P-47s and they totally destroyed the train.

By mid-May, excitement was at a high level regarding the upcoming invasion. Until then, I had been able to occasionally telephone Sarah and I wrote her several times each week but, suddenly, we were restricted to base, no telephone calls allowed, and our mail was being held. It was essential that the invasion plans be kept secret and, even though we pilots and crews had no idea of specifically when or where the invasion would take place,

Headquarters wanted to be sure no one even shared guesses.

On May 23, we again escorted bombers, but not to Germany. We attacked rail centers in France and Belgium, and on the 27th we went back and attacked rail centers in Germany. Over 1000 bombers and more than 300 P-51s were involved and we encountered no German fighters.

For the next week, we flew escort, escort, escort, all over Germany and Belgium. The Luftwaffe did come up and amazing swirls of dogfights took place. Nearly 700 American fighters were involved in each mission and the sky was crowded. I just kept shooting.

May ended and June began, but I didn't even know what day today is, let alone what month—May? June? I just keep flying and keep shooting. I'm tired.

D-DAY

The 336th Fighter Group didn't fly on June 1; our planes needed attention and we pilots needed some rest. On June 2, we were called to a "Top Secret Briefing" led by our Group C.O, Colonel Martinson. This type of meeting didn't happen very often, so we were all a-buzz.

"Men," he began, "this meeting is just what it says—a TOP SECRET meeting!" He looked around slowly to make sure we understood what he said. "Please pay careful attention to what I say--your life might depend upon it."

He gathered his thoughts and continued, obviously speaking very carefully.

"Our role will undergo a dramatic change for the next little while. We are going to embark upon a series of actions code-named "CHATTANOOGA CHOO-CHOO". I see your smiles, but we won't be singing any songs. Obviously this has to do with trains. We have been conducting various attacks on enemy trains when we find them on our way home from our escort jobs, but henceforth, our efforts will be much more specific and coordinated. The Ninth Air Force and our British friends are working together as the Tactical Air Force with the goal of completely disrupting enemy transportation in western France. We will now be doing the same thing in eastern France. There will be continuous air cover in the area throughout the daylight hours and airborne controllers will direct you to your targets."

I glanced over at Jim Stafford and he looked back at me and—winked!

The Colonel continued: "These efforts are vital for the success of" (pause) "an upcoming action that will happen" (another, longer pause) "sometime soon."

It didn't take a genius to figure out that the big invasion must be coming up.

The Colonel finished: "I have full confidence that each of you will perform to your usual splendid level. God be with you and—remember, this TOP SECRET!"

* * * * * * *

We started our "train-ride" that afternoon by heading for the Chaumont area. We got our first call very soon after we arrived. Major Stafford received the call and sent Red Flight south toward Dijon to attack a reported westbound freight train. Sure enough, it was right where it was supposed to be. We flew a careful circle around it, searching for any telltale "big crates" or tarpaulins that might hide anti-aircraft guns and, surprisingly, didn't see any. As the train moved slowly out from behind some forest and got completely in the clear, it did something strange—it stopped! We saw the engine crew jump off the locomotive and run into the woods and a couple of guys from the rear end did too. (Interesting note: what we call a "caboose" is here called a "guard's van". Strange language, this English we speak!) It seemed as though they were getting out of our way so we could destroy the train without hurting them. I was very suspicious, but decided to make the first attack to see what happened. I had the other guys circle while I went in; it wasn't necessary to destroy the engine to stop the train, so I dove in low and fast from straight ahead of the train and I flew along the length of it, raking it with my six 'fifties. No response from the ground, so I queued up the guys and we took turns really ripping that train apart. After several passes, fires were burning and there were a couple of explosions that might have been ammunition went off. Then, one last pass by Rustler who concentrated on a

160

particular box car that refused to burn. Just as he really poured the gunfire to it, it suddenly erupted in a huge explosion that even shook our airplanes. He came out the other side and reported he was undamaged. We were amazed to see that where the car had been, three other railcars had disappeared and there was a huge crater in the ground. Wow! That must have contained bombs or something.

When the dust settled (literally!), I was astonished to see the train's crewmen come hesitantly out to the edge of the woods. They were waving a small French flag and cheering! That made the war a lot more personal for me. I formed up Red Flight and we did a low, fast pass past the crew and I wagged my wings as we passed. I will always remember that experience!

White, Blue, and Yellow Flights all hit targets, too, until the controller released us with a final assignment to strafe a small rail yard in Troyes, which we did.

June 3 was a day of repairs and rest. We all got a laugh as the mechanics pulled pieces of a French railway car out of Rustler's plane. Funny, but we're glad he's OK and the magnificent P-51 got him home.

The next day we escorted B-17s as they attacked the railway bridge at Massey, France—no action for us, though.

We were scheduled for a very early morning briefing on June 5, but it was cancelled because of bad weather over the Continent. A bit later, the rumor was passing around that the invasion had been scheduled for the fifth but had been delayed due to the weather. Wow! It appears that the big invasion really is going happen—soon!

At about mid-morning, I was summoned to my airplane to meet with Pappy. I was worried something was wrong with the aircraft at just the wrong time. I walked out to the flight line and Pappy was waiting by my beautiful Mustang.

"Good Morning, Lieutenant!"

"Good Morning, Pappy. What's up? I hope the airplane is O.K.!"

"Oh, the plane is fine, sir."

"Then what's this about?" That's when I noticed that Pappy looked a bit uncomfortable.

"Come on, Mister Crew Chief, you look like you got caught raiding Red's freezer. What's up?"

Then Len and Larry appeared, also unusually quiet. As they gathered around me, I looked to Pappy to explain.

"Well, sir—we—uh—want to—ah—talk with you about something."

I couldn't imagine what was wrong.

"Well, go ahead—you've never been shy before!"

Pappy took a deep breath. "Well, it's like this—we just got an order to paint big black and white stripes on the wings and fuselage of all the planes. I hear it's so the American and British soldiers will be able to tell us apart from the Nazis and not shoot at you."

I responded with a smile, "Well, that sounds like a great idea to me! I'd hate to get shot down by some farmer from Indiana!"

The guys chuckled, but there was still obviously something else.

"Ah, come on guys, what's with you?"

Finally, Pappy bucked up and told me what they were all wrought up about.

"O.K., sir, here it is—you know how some of the other squadrons have been painting up their airplanes with names and stuff, but Colonel Martinson wouldn't let us do that?"

I nodded. I thought it was sort of a silly regulation, but that's what the boss said, so we kept our planes unadorned.

Pappy smiled. "Well, we just got a message from Eighth Fighter Command 'suggesting' that naming the planes and adding markings for how many missions or how many kills has proven to be a big aid to morale, so we should 'consider' doing the same. Colonel Martinson shrugged and gave us the OK."

I thought about it for a moment—mostly for effect—and then grinned, "Sounds good to me!"

Pappy spoke up: "Uh, well, Sir, we have a suggestion for a name—but, of course, you can name it anything you want, after your Mom, or Sarah, or something."

Actually, I had given passing thought to what I might name the plane, if we ever got permission, and I had seriously considered naming it "Sweet Sarah". But a moment's thought quickly indicated that if I got shot down, shooting down "Sweet Sarah" might not be a good omen—after all—shooting down Sarah? Nope!"

"Well, guys, what do you suggest?"

Larry spoke up. "Sir, there's guy with the 339th who's quite an artist and he said he could paint us a picture."

I must have looked confused.

Pappy stepped in. "Sir, because we all call the plane 'the J-Bird', we thought that would be a good name, and this artist guy will paint a picture of a tough-looking Woody Woodpecker kind of bird looking like a bandit with a fifty-caliber machine gun under each wing—or arm—or whatever. We think it might turn out really good." He ended on a hopeful note.

I considered the idea and it actually sounded pretty clever.

"O.K., guys, go ahead and get the J-Bird painted up! Can you get it done in time for the paint to dry for tomorrow's mission? I have a feeling tomorrow might be a big day."

"Oh, yeah!" exclaimed Len. "Oops! I mean 'Yes, Sir'—sir".

* * * * * *

Late that afternoon there was a bit of weak sunshine, so I wandered over to see how the great art project was coming along. As I approached the airplane, there was a person devoting his full concentration to painting a picture on the cowling beneath the exhaust stacks. He must have just finished because, as I approached, he sat back and looked carefully at his work. When I got close enough to see I was astounded—it was a magnificent rendering just as Pappy had described. A mean-looking bandit-bird festooned with bandoleers of ammunition and brandishing a fifty-caliber gun under each arm. The bird was black and the various details were red, yellow, and blue. It was awesome! And curving just above it in a red cartoon script edged in yellow was the name "J-Bird".

"Incredible!" I exclaimed.

The artist hadn't heard me arrive so he jumped at the sound of my voice.

"Oh! Sorry, sir, I didn't know you were there!"

"No problem. This is masterful work! Thank you!"

A smile graced his paint-stained face. "That's O.K., Sir, your crew said they're paying for it! So you must be the pilot— 'Lucky'?

Before I could answer, my three guys came jogging up.

164

"How's it look, Sir?" Said Pappy between panting breaths.

"Incredible! I absolutely love it!" And then, realizing I didn't know the artist's name, I turned to him. "Well, Mr. Artist, you've done great work! May I know your name to congratulate you formally?"

"I'm Sergeant Williamson from the 339th. I'm glad you like it. Also, sir, did you notice by the cockpit?"

I was so taken with the artwork I hadn't noted anything else. I looked up to the cockpit and there it was, lettered in beautiful letters just below the cockpit combing: 'Lt. Thomas 'Lucky' Peters."

"Very nice, Sarge! Thanks!" Then I noticed something else.

"Uh, guys? What's all this?" I pointed to a double row of small red and black swastikas painted on the side just ahead and below the cockpit.

Pappy smiled so big I thought he'd pop. "Those are your confirmed kills, Sir."

"What?! There are"—I counted carefully—"twelve of them! Where did you get that outlandish number?"

The guys all grinned. "Sir, we talked with Lieutenant-Colonel Liebowitz and he checked your file—twelve confirmed aerial victories! You're a double-ace, Sir!"

I couldn't help but detect the pride the guys felt at the success of "their" airplane—and pilot.

I was really abashed and almost speechless. "Fellas, I'm so shocked you could knock me over with a feather! I note them in my log book, but I haven't gone back to add them up. I'm in shock!"

That elicited a round a good-natured laughter and some back-slapping.

You know, I thought, With great guys like these, we can't help but win this war!

* * * * * *

It's a good thing it was fast-drying paint; the next morning—June 6, 1944—we were up early and on our way to Eastern France to support the greatest invasion in the history of the world. It was dark when we left, and we flew too far north and east to see the ships, but I was told later they covered the sea from horizon to horizon.

We patrolled from Metz to Nancy to Dijon, seeking anything that moved. One of the guys from Blue Flight even went after a motorcyclist on the road! We were sent to investigate a reported military convoy approaching a road junction near Neufchateau. All of Red Flight went and, sure enough, there was a short line of seven grey-green German military trucks scurrying toward the junction of six highways located right in town. I decided it would be best to hit the convoy as soon before the town as possible because if they made it to town, they could hide amongst the buildings. As a result, we went right after them as soon as we saw them.

I divided the flight into two parts, I would take Jim with me and we would attack from the front, attempting to stop the convoy and block the road. Rustler and Reb would attack from the up-sun side immediately after Jim and I cleared. This was another instance where I wished we'd been equipped with bombs or rockets, but we were still in "escort-mode" and just carried our usual armament and the ever-present drop tanks of fuel. None the less, four Mustangs with six 'fifties apiece can do a lot of damage! In we went—

I circled in and went after the lead truck with the intention of at least stopping it and—I hoped—possibly turning it to block the road. In low and fast, but not TOO low. (We had learned that if you attacked from too low an altitude, you limited the amount of target you had to focus on and it was better to have a bit of a dive angle so you could adjust your fire.) Some of the soldiers jumped off the trucks and fled down the road embankment where they could try to shoot at us, and others just hunkered down in the road and started shooting. I squeezed the trigger on my stick and the beautiful sound of six powerful machineguns began. It was usually too noisy to hear them, but I could I could always *feel* them firing. I walked my stream into the truck and held it there as long as I could. As I began to level and pass over it, I kept firing along the truck and the one behind it. As I pulled out, Jim hit some on the front truck but he focused mostly on the second one. Then we were clear and Red Three and Four came in from the side. Jim and I turned and approached for a second pass, this time from the rear. And so it went, Red Flight was performing a perfectly coordinated attack. After that second pass, I assigned Jim to take on the enemy soldiers on the right of the road and I took the left. After all, enemy trucks don't kill American soldiers, enemy soldiers do. In short order, that convoy ceased to be a threat to the fellows coming ashore far to the west of us.

That's how we spent the famous "D-Day", shooting up anything that moved in our assigned zone. We went after trucks, cars, trains, even a tank! When our fuel and ammunition started to become a concern, we were released and headed for home. I was very, very tempted to fly over the invasion beaches to see what it all looked like, but I quickly gave up the idea. We had been briefed that the air above the beaches was so crowded that specific assignments were issued for very specific times. Sightseers were definitely NOT welcome! One funny thing did happen on the way home, though. As we approached Soissons, a ground-based controller called for any available aircraft in that area. I responded that I had four P-51s with a bit of ammo left, could we help?

The controller reported that a high-ranking officer in a staff car was reported to be rushing towards the invasion area and could we stop him? You bet! I got the location where the staff car was last seen and off we went. We caught up to him as he passed through Couloisy and as I was deciding how to attack him, the irrepressible Reb drawled over the radio, "Kin ah go git 'em, Sir? Ah'd love to stop him!"

Oh, well, why not, I thought.

"O.K, Red Three, go get 'em!"

The driver of that staff car must have been a race-car driver before the war—he swerved and jinked that car in amazing ways and watching Reb try to hit him was like watching a boy try to hit his first running jackrabbit. Even though we knew it was a life-and-death chase for the Germans in the car, the sight of that car leading Reb all over the place was really quite funny. Finally, Reb had scored enough hits that the car seemed to be disabled and it coasted to a stop. Out jumped two Germans, one of them dressed ready for a parade. They scampered down the road embankment and what must have been the enlisted-grade driver pulled out his pistol and started shooting at Reb. Then things got even funnier—the officer started pointing and hopping around and waving his arms, obviously trying to give orders to the other guy—who promptly ignored him and kept shooting. It would have made a good Hollywood comedy, but enough is enough. I guess the driver must have run out of ammo because he stopped shooting and both Germans quickly retreated into some nearby woods where we couldn't get at them. I recalled Reb and I reported the events to the controller.

"Oh, well," said the Controller in a gentle English-girl voice, "nice try fellows. At least he'll be walking for while. Thanks, anyway."

On the 7th, we were up early, as usual, and we escorted some B-17s to Lisieu. We got back to Fowlmere late in the morning and we were sent out again, this time to patrol the beachhead and stop any German efforts to reinforce their troops. The thing I remember most is the sight of all the ships and landing craft and all the soldiers swarming across the beach. Some of the ships had been shelled and some were sunk and others were burning. But we could see the Army wasn't pinned down on the beach and they were moving slowly forward. We were called for a couple of strafing missions but, overall, the Allies had total air superiority over the beaches and what was needed was pin-point assistance in ground attack. I hate to admit it, but the 501st wasn't really at its best in that ultra-precise role.

On the 8th, we were among 526 P-51s (!) that ranged across Northwestern France to disrupt enemy communications. We were one of the lucky squadrons that actually encountered enemy fighters in the air. Six FW-190s tried to bounce us near Evreux. Major Stafford sent Red and Blue flights to take them on. Eight P-51s against six FW-190s is a fairly even contest, but these pilots weren't among the Luftwaffe's best. Their leader hesitated as we approached and that allowed us to define the flow of the combat. Blue Flight circled to the enemy's left and I took Red Flight to their right. Two of the Germans broke left and crossed right in front of us. Jim was better positioned that I was, so he opened fire. He tracked right on the 190 with the black numeral "7" on its fuselage. Lots of pieces came off and down he went. Score another one for Jim! Reb and Rustler circled a bit further out and the second guy met up them. As I turned to assist, all I saw was a 190 arcing down on fire. Good job, Red Flight! A little later, Captain Jim got a 109 for a total of three for 501st out of a total of 27 claimed in the air.

On June 9 and 10, the weather was lousy and we stayed home—I even managed to finally get a call through to Sarah. Talking with her was wonderful, but I really missed being with her.

On the 11th, we escorted some B-17s to Pontaubault Bridge but we were just along for moral support—no action for us.

On the 12th, we flew fighter sweeps in the Rennes area, but nothing noteworthy happened for Red Flight.

On June 13, 1944, my world almost ended.

DOODLEBUGS

An event of historical importance happened on June 13, 1944 that also had a profound impact on me.

Germany had been working on various "secret weapons" that Hitler promised would change the war. Allied intelligence had learned of some disturbing developments through information provided by spies within France, Germany, and throughout occupied Europe that had been verified by photo reconnaissance. In fact, Eighth Air Force bombers had been conducting "Project Crossbow" attacks on strange facilities that were cropping up along the French coast that were reported to be launching sites of some sort of pilotless flying weapon. I didn't learn any of this, however, until after June 13.

The weather on Tuesday, June 13 was lousy, as usual. The 501st was sent out that morning to escort bombers to attack the Dreux Airfield in France. It was a routine mission for us and we didn't have any excitement. When we landed back at Fowlmere, I headed for our hut with hopes of taking a wonderful (cold) shower. As I neared the hut, a Corporal came breathlessly up to me and, between panting breaths, told me Colonel Martinson wanted to see me right away. I figured "right away" meant "right away", so I just turned and went over to his office still wearing my flying gear. I couldn't imagine what I'd done to warrant being called to the Group C.O's office, so I was a bit nervous when I arrived there. His clerk told me to go right in—which added to my nervousness. I entered and approached his desk and reported just like we learned 'way back in Cadet training.

"Relax, Peters. I understand you are very close to a lady named Brockman, Sarah Brockman?"

My heart nearly stopped—why is he asking me about Sarah?

"Yes, sir. She's the most wonderful girl in the world. Oops! Sorry, sir! I mean she's my girlfriend."

The Colonel had a pained expression that really frightened me.

"Uh, Sir, is there something about Sarah?"

Martinson nodded. "Yes. Peters. We received a call from a Mrs. Breese at Miss Brockman's employer. There was some sort of explosion that went off near your Sarah and she has been injured and is in the hospital."

I thought I'd collapse.

"Get a hold of yourself, son. We'll be standing down for a couple of days and I'm sure you'll want to visit her. Here— " He handed me a five day pass effective immediately.

I don't know if I even thanked him—I just took off at a run for my hut to get changed and get myself on the way to London. *There'd better not be any face cloth shipments today!*

Nonetheless, I was surprised when I exited the hut a few minutes later to find Pappy standing there with a concerned look on his face. "I just heard, Lieutenant. I have a jeep and we can leave for London right now."

"A Jeep!? You mean you'll drive me all the way to London?"

"Yes, sir. Do you know what hospital she's in?"

I felt like a dummy because I hadn't thought to ask the Colonel. I looked at the pass slip and turned it over to see if there was a clue. Sure enough, on the back the Colonel had written "Mile End Hospital, Bancroft Road, London. Room 237."

"Pappy, do you know where 'Mile End' is in London?"

"Nope. Never heard of it."

"Well, she's in the Mile End Hospital on Bancroft Road."

"Then let's get you to London and you can get a cab to take you there—or get directions."

"Let's go!"

And go we did. A Jeep is not a comfortable vehicle, and it is not built for speed, but Pappy nursed it up to a rather frightening velocity and I just held on for dear life. Also, for the first time in many years, I prayed. I prayed for Sarah—and I prayed for Pappy and me.

*　*　*　*　*　*

With the indulgence of a couple of English policemen and one American MP, we managed to get to greater London in one piece. Finding London wasn't difficult—it's one of the largest cities in the world—but finding Mile End Hospital took some doing. We would stop and ask directions of whomever we encountered and each one would inch us closer to our goal. Finally, after a drawn out process, we thought we might be getting close, but my nerves were on end and my patience was long since shredded. We had pulled up to a stop at a major intersection when an ever-present black London taxi pulled up next to us. I shouted across to the driver asking him the way to the hospital and his response surprised me.

"Mile End, eh?"

"Yes."

"Don't know yer way 'round 'eer?"

"No."

A thoughtful pause.

"Well, lad, you'd best jump in here with me so's I can take you there straightaway."

That didn't require a moment's thought from me and I quickly joined him. The "Bobby" controlling traffic let us go and away we went. I lost track of my amazing crew chief but I figured the incredibly industrious Pappy would be fine.

Arrival at the hospital was a blur but, despite my confusion, I was directed to the second floor and the nurse's station for the "Orthopaedic Unit" as the sign above the desk said.

The middle-aged nurse at the desk looked up at me expectantly, so I asked for patient Sarah Brockman. I looked at my note and added "She's supposed to be room 237."

A brief flicker of amusement crossed her face.

"Miss Brockman, eh?"

"Yes, M'am."

She paused for a second. "Would you happen to be a—she looked down at a paper on her desk—Lieutenant Peters?"

I was shocked. "Uh, Yes, M'am, I'm Lieutenant Peters. Thomas Peters."

She smiled. "From the moment Miss Brockman arrived early this morning, in her delirium, she's continued to repeat your name. We wondered what that was all about. We didn't know if you were a friend, or someone else injured in the blast. Frankly, we've been rather worried, so I'm happy to know you are hale and hearty."

"Yes, Sarah and I are friends—special friends. But I'm frantic—I just survived a hair-raising drive here from Fowlmere in a Jeep driven by a maniac and I'm terrified about Sarah. Is she O.K.?"

174

This time her expression sobered. She answered in measured tones, every bit the professional nurse.

"Miss Brockman was injured in a rather mysterious early-morning blast. She suffered various contusions and cuts and she has three broken ribs and a simple fracture of her left ulna."

I must have looked perplexed.

"The Ulna is a bone in your forearm. A simple fracture is a clean break that didn't break the skin. The doctors were able to set the break. Her ribs are taped and there are plasters over her many cuts."

That was all fine, but I still needed to know: "But will she be O.K.?"

After a thoughtful pause, "Yes, we expect her to recover fully, barring any unexpected infection. She has been under a strong sedative that is just beginning to wear off, so she is still very groggy."

"May I visit her?"

"Yes, but keep it short, she needs rest."

I found Room 237 and went quietly through the door. The bundle of bandages and "plasters" lying in the bed simply could not be my Sarah! I approached the bed and, as I could see her lovely face, was relieved to confirm that, yes, this IS my lovely Sarah—just a very beat-up version.

Her eyes were closed, but she rolled slightly and groaned.

"Sarah?" I asked quietly.

Another groan, or maybe it was a mumble.

"Sarah, its Tom."

"Tom", she mumbled.

Her eyes fluttered and slowly opened a bit. She was obviously not able to focus or, perhaps, even think clearly.

"Tom, is that you?"

"Yes, sweetheart, it's me."

She mumbled something and closed her eyes, apparently falling back asleep.

I know the nurse said I should "keep my visit short", but I wasn't about to leave the bedside of my darling Sarah. I resolved to simply stay in the chair by her bed and, if the hospital tried to throw me out, they'd learn how stubborn an Oklahoma rancher can be.

We had been doing a lot of flying and I was very tired, so I must have dozed off in the chair.

Sometime later, a different nurse came into the room and that must have wakened me. Much to my surprise, a groggy, but familiar voice greeted me.

"Well, sleeping beauty, it appears the American Air Force is not allowing you enough rest!"

"Sarah! You're awake!"

"Yes," Sarah chuckled weakly, "I awoke to find a handsome flyer sleeping beside my bed."

"Oh, Sweetheart, I've been frantic since I heard you were injured!"

"Yes," she joked, "I see how frantic—since the first thing you do is fall asleep!"

I knew she was kidding and I smiled ruefully. "You were sleeping and I just knew I wasn't going to budge until you woke up. But, yes, we've been exhaustingly busy, so I guess I drifted off."

Sarah looked thoughtful: "Tom, how did you know about this? How did you find me? How did you get here? How

176

did you get time off?" Then a stricken look crossed her face. "Oh, Tom, you didn't desert, did you?"

"Whoa, honey! First, no, I didn't desert. The Colonel gave me a five-day pass. As to the other, Mrs. Breese called the Colonel and told him. When we landed from our morning mission, he called me in and told me. I nearly fainted!"

"How on earth did you get here?"

I laughed. "The ever-resourceful Pappy heard what had happened to you, got a Jeep from somewhere, and drove me here. I'm lucky to be alive—he drives like a maniac! But after much ado, here I am. And..." I added, "...I'm not going anywhere until you get out of here!"

I could see she was getting tired again, so I refrained from asking my own list of questions. After consulting the nurse and Sarah, it was decided I should find nearby lodging and return first thing tomorrow. The prognosis was that Sarah would be much better after a good night's sleep, allowing the sedative to wear off. So, reluctantly, I said goodbye and left.

I went down the stairs and started to cross the lobby to leave the hospital when a voice stopped me short.

"Lieutenant, is she going to be O.K.?"

It was Pappy!

"How in the world do you do it, Pappy? You always turn up at the strangest places at the just the right time!"

He grinned. "Well, sir, you may be 'Lucky' and all that, but it seems like *somebody* should keep an eye on you. The other guys and I don't want to have to trust a new pilot with our J-bird!"

We laughed, and then he explained: "I just followed the cab here and hung around 'til you came down. Chasing that cab was something else, I tell you!"

177

We asked some of the hospital staff about nearby lodging and we were directed to a small boarding house run by a Mrs. Paulson. She agreed to take us in and we soon enjoyed a "boarding house" dinner (called "supper" here) that was very family-like and we enjoyed meeting our fellow boarders. Pappy seemed especially to enjoy meeting Mrs. Paulson's grown daughter Eloise. (Don't be nervous—Pappy isn't married. He once told me he couldn't see how a career in air force and being married would work together.)

The next morning I was on my way to the hospital right after breakfast. Up to Sarah's room, where I was surprised to find another visitor already there—a young lady about Sarah's age, with dark brown hair and a very serious face.

Sarah seemed much more in her right mind, although I thought she might be experiencing some pain.

"Hello. Tom. I'd like you to meet my friend Effie."

Effie didn't seem particularly overjoyed to meet me, but I decided I'd be friendly, anyway. You know, "Any friend of Sarah's is a friend of mine".

Sarah went on to explain: "Effie and I have been great friends for years. We had a birthday party for a friend at Effie's flat Monday night and, when it got too late, I just decided to stay the night with her. I was leaving early Tuesday morning to get to work when the explosion happened."

I nodded in understanding.

Sarah went on. "Thankfully, Effie wasn't injured, although her flat was damaged."

I must have looked quizzical, because Effie shared her story: "I had just walked to the door with Sarah and, as she was leaving, I went back upstairs to my 'loo. I was in there when the explosion happened. All of my windows were blown out and, if I'd still been in bed, I would have been seriously cut up." She shuddered as she finished.

"Wow! That was a close call!" I responded.

But I was more than curious about "the explosion".

"Sarah, Effie, there seems to be some mystery about this explosion that sent you here. What was it? Did a bomber come over? Or did one of those sneak fighter attacks happen? Maybe an unexploded bomb?"

The girls looked at each other.

"Tom, we've just been discussing that. The anti-aircraft guns started firing, but neither of us heard the sound of bombers. Also, there weren't any UXBs in the neighborhood."

I waited for Sarah to continue.

She looked again at Effie, and then continued. "The only thing I noticed as I went out the door was a sort 'buzzing' sound overhead--sort of a 'buzz-buzz-buzz'. Then the sound stopped so I turned to pull the door shut and that's when the explosion happened. I must have been blown against the open door and that's what broke my arm and ribs."

Effie added: "When the explosion happened, I knew Sarah was probably hit by it, so I rushed downstairs and, sure enough, there she was, all crumpled up on the ground with the door half-round her. I yelled for help and soon an ARP warden came and he called an ambulance. I only live few blocks from here, so they got Sarah here quickly."

Effie looked fondly at Sarah. "I'm so happy you'll be all right! I couldn't bear the thought that you'd been killed— especially at my house!" Effie paused, and then added with strong feeling, "I hate this war and I hate the Germans!"

She said it with such force that I must have looked startled. Sarah noticed.

"Tom," she said gently, "Effie was in Coventry."

I looked blank.

"Tom, Coventry—the city. You know about Coventry?"

I shook my head. "Coventry? No, I don't know anything about Coventry." I looked helplessly at both girls.

Effie responded with such anger I was speechless. "You don't know about Coventry? You stupid Americans! You wait to get into the war until you've bankrupted us! You don't know anything about our country or our history! Then you show up acting like the saviors of the world. I think the saying going around is true—'The only problem with the Americans is they are over-paid, over-sexed, and over here'! I can't stand the lot of you!"

Sarah seemed shocked, too. She spoke gently, trying to calm her friend: "Effie? Please?"

Effie made an effort to calm herself, but didn't say anything.

Sarah tried to explain.

"Tom, on the night of November 14, 1940, the Germans attacked the city of Coventry with a rain of bombs and incendiaries that destroyed virtually the entire city, including the 14th century Cathedral. The purpose of the attack was solely to destroy the city, which they did."

I was stunned. "What! They attacked *civilians*? On purpose? They blew up a church? That's grotesque!" And then I remembered the housing areas in Liverpool we'd seen when we first arrived. "Oh. Lord", I said, "I just remembered the burned-out neighborhoods we saw in Liverpool."

I was obviously shocked.

Effie then spoke, in a soft, quiet voice so filled with sadness it wrenched my heart.

"My dad worked at the Victor Magneto plant and we lived on Gosford Street. That was right in the center of the attack. We had an Anderson shelter in the garden area out back, and father hurried us out there when it became apparent the attack was a big one. We were all in there, Mother, father, my younger brother Len, and me."

I was afraid to hear the rest of the story.

Effie continued. "We were O.K. through most of the night. We figured our house had probably been damaged, but the incendiaries didn't hurt our shelter, and the HE was landing farther away. Then, at about 3 AM, we heard another lot of bombers over head and we heard a stick of high-explosive bombs start landing closer and closer."

Tears were streaming down her cheeks as she spoke.

"One of the bombs landed just behind our shelter and there was a terrific crash and a blast of hot air. Hours later, the rescuers found me buried in the debris. Everyone else was killed."

I was so choked up I couldn't have spoken, even if I'd known what to say. I was so distressed I think it worried Sarah.

"Tom?"

I just waved my hand. I couldn't speak.

After a few moments, Effie composed herself. "That's what happened to Coventry," she stated quietly.

Sarah spoke. "Tom, you really never heard of Coventry?"

I shook my head. I started thinking back to Mid-November, 1940. "No, I was in college. That would have been just before Thanksgiving, so I would have been studying for my term final exams. That was my third year at college. I just didn't have time to follow the news."

I looked at Effie. "Effie, I'm so sorry. I just don't know what to say..."

The room was quiet.

Sarah spoke again, quietly.

"Tom, it's not only Coventry. They attacked London every night for months on end. That was terrible enough, but then, on the night of December 29, 1940, they sent a huge attack that lasted all night. They tried to wipe out the heart of London the way they had Coventry. Right *here* in London!"

I looked at her. "You mean *right* here? Like right *here*?"

The girls nodded grimly. Sarah explained: "Yes. They did the same thing here, over the oldest, most historic part of London that stretches from here clear over past where I live. You may have heard the center of the London referred to as 'The City'?"

I had, so I nodded.

"Well, the same area is also called 'The Square Mile'. Where we are sitting right now is at the traditional edge of it, so this district is called 'Mile End'."

That was interesting, but the story of an attack on where Sarah lives? That was serious!

"Tom, you know I live on Chapel Street in a district called 'Moorgate'?"

I nodded.

"Well, the same thing happened to us on December 29 as happened to Coventry on November 14—only with even more incendiaries. The intention was to burn the city down. All of the destruction you see throughout London is not by accident. The destruction is not caused by bombs that 'missed' their target. Those bombs HIT their target! Us!"

I was overwhelmed by emotion—anger, sadness, incredulity, fear for Sarah.

"Sarah," I asked, "Were you in the midst of it like Effie was?" I was afraid of the answer.

She answered in a patient, gentle voice. "Tom, this is not the first time I've been in the hospital."

"You mean...?"

"Yes. During that attack on the 29th, I was home in my flat, planning to wash my hair. I no longer live in that flat because--" long pause—"it no longer exists."

She went on. "It was a terrible attack that just went on and on. The sirens sounded a little after 6 PM and soon we could see fires starting up along the river. But the planes just kept coming and fire spread through the center of the city. Soon the bombers were getting closer and closer to our neighborhood and the fires kept coming, too. By 9 PM, it looked like the entire city was burning, so several of us decided it would be wise to go to the shelter in the basement of the office block around the corner from us. By midnight, it was getting unusually hot in the shelter when a warden came and told us to evacuate. He told us the building over our heads was completely on fire, as were all of the adjoining buildings. He led us up and out and the sight we saw when we emerged was breathtaking. Raging fires everywhere, firemen struggling with hoses and shouting instructions to one another, debris clogging all the streets—it was unbelievable. Now I know what Dante's inferno looks and feels like!"

She went on. "The warden led us through the mess and was trying to get us to another shelter that hadn't been compromised yet. There were thirty or forty people in the group and, somehow I ended up last. As we turned a corner, I heard the firemen yell 'look out!' and they all scrambled away from a building on my right. The wall of that building gave way and collapsed into the street. I was struck by some of the debris. I woke up later in the hospital. Frankly, I'm getting tired of waking up in hospitals!"

I was shocked and angry. Intentionally attacking civilians was sickening. Effie must have figured out what I was thinking.

"Tom—that's your name, right?"

I nodded.

"Tom, these attacks on our cities and people are nothing new. They've been going on since Autumn of 1940—we call it the 'Blitz'; have you heard of that?"

I had, although I hadn't thought much about it.

"Well, the Germans thought if they attacked innocent civilians, we'd rebel against our government and ask for peace. It didn't work."

She looked at me intently. "Tom, I don't mean to be cruel, but the Germans aren't the only ones bombing cities."

"What!?"

"That's right. Every night, our RAF bombers go to Germany and do what is euphemistically called 'Area Bombing'. There's supposed to be a factory or war business somewhere in there, but they just bomb the general area. That's just a pretty name for bombing cities, hoping the civilians will tire of being blasted and push their government to end the war. That's just like what they did to us—and just like here, it doesn't work."

I thought about our American bombing being 'strategic' bombing of specific military targets. Effie must have read my mind.

"Tom, Sarah tells me you are a fighter pilot who escorts bombers to attack Germany, is that right?"

Again, I nodded. I wondered, *What is she getting at?*

"When you get to Berlin, or wherever, and the weather is bad and you can't see the ground, what do your bombers do?"

I was picturing it in my mind and hesitated in answering her.

"Do they turn around and come back?"

"No," I had to admit.

"Do they leave and go after another target?"

"Yes, usually."

"And if there are clouds there and they can't see?"

There was something that had bothered me for a long time, but I just refused to think about it, and now Effie forced me to. I didn't like the answer.

She could see my sudden revulsion.

"That's right, Tom. You start out to attack a precise target, but even when you CAN see, the bombs scatter all across the city nearby—don't they?"

I couldn't look her in the eyes.

"And when the weather is bad, and the German fighters are swarming all over the bombers, they often just drop them 'somewhere close' to the target and then turn quickly for home. Isn't that right?"

I was sick to my stomach. I suddenly realized how heinous war really is.

185

This discussion was really very unpleasant for me, and Sarah could tell.

"Tom, we're not trying to make you feel bad. We're simply telling you what we've been through since September, 1939. That's nearly four years of this. Fortunately, the non-stop attacks on our cities have let up although occasionally we get caught by a lone fighter dropping a bomb somewhere. This thing that hit me might be something new, though, and that's a concern."

I thought hard about it all.

Effie spoke up. "You have to remember that we didn't start this war and neither did you. But now we're all in it together. Both Churchill and Roosevelt have stated that we are fighting to save western civilization. That's fancy talk but, Tom, its true! "

Sarah added: "It IS true, Tom. There has been a terrible evil unleashed throughout the world and we have to stop it. England can't do it alone and we're glad you're here to help us."

I couldn't help but smile. "I'm not so sure Effie is glad we're here..."

She looked at me, and smiled a thin smile. "I'm sorry I took it out on you and I AM glad you're here. I just wish you all understood better and weren't so arrogant! But we need you, and this invasion we just launched is both horrible and wonderful at the same time. Tom, we've just GOT to beat them!"

I again expressed my admiration at the amazing courage of the English people.

Sarah responded, "Tom, it's not amazing courage. We're just as afraid as anyone, but we've learned to go on with life, and we are resolutely determined to beat them. I don't want to live in a world like theirs!"

Effie leaned forward towards me. "Tom, it's not courage. We've just learned to face each new day determined to 'get on with it' as cheerfully as possible."

I have just learned an important new lesson for life, I thought to myself, *to 'just get on with it as cheerfully as possible.' Wow!*

There followed a few moments of thoughtful silence, finally broken by Sarah's chuckle.

"Well, we're a fine bunch, aren't we? Maybe now that we've solved how to win the war, we can move on to pleasanter things—like when do I get out of here!"

It turned out that "getting out of here" wasn't quite as soon as we hoped. The doctors wanted to be sure that no infection would set in, so she stayed "in hospital" for a bit longer. Finally, on Thursday evening, she was released with orders for follow-up care later. Pappy and I assisted her—very gently and carefully—into our jeep and took her home.

A CONCERN, INDEED!

That Thursday was a big day for another reason.

According to news reports, the "explosion" that struck Mile End at about 4:30 AM on June 13 that injured Sarah and killed eight others was one of five "flying bombs" that were launched toward London. The Germans had devised a pilotless flying bomb that was literally a bomb with wings and an engine. The engine was a pulse-jet type that made the distinctive sound Sarah heard—a buzz-buzz-buzz sound. When the engine shut off, the bomb dived to earth and blew up whatever was there.

Nothing much else happened on that front until Thursday; while Sarah was getting ready to go home from the hospital, a new flurry of the "Buzz Bombs", or "Doodlebugs", as they came to be called, were launched at London. As Sarah said, "it was cause for concern".

On that Thursday, more than sixty of the bombs struck London and it was about to get worse.

The last two days of my pass were spent taking care of our invalid. Pappy and I moved in to Sarah's flat, which made it crowded, but we wanted to be sure she was taken care of. Pappy surprised me at how gentle and caring he could be. He seemed to adopt Sarah as his special patient and he treated her like a queen. I couldn't get close to her without his asking in a concerned tone "Is she all right?"

Effie managed to arrange her work so she could spend time helping Sarah after we left so, following a parting that was very difficult for me, Pappy and I headed our noisy green jeep back towards Fowlmere.

*   *   *   *   *   *

188

We got back to base Saturday night. Sunday morning, I was notified that there was a special formation meeting scheduled for three o'clock that afternoon and we should all wear our   Class A uniform.

Oh, brother, I thought, *That's just what I need. An inspection when I just got back from London. Great!*

At the appointed hour, we all met on the flight line in front of the airplanes and formed up by squadrons and flights. Colonel Martinson and his staff appeared before us and the Colonel made a speech.

"Men," he began, "the 336th Fighter group has been in combat now for six months. We have helped to initiate a new model of airplane, the P-51, into combat and it has become the standard for excellence in long-distance bomber escort. We have also helped prove the airplane's versatility by flying escort, strafing, train-busting, and even..." he paused and smiled over at Jim Stafford "...chasing enemy staff cars for fun and profit."

Obviously the story of Reb chasing the German car had become popular knowledge and everyone burst out laughing at the Colonel's comment. Reb just smiled ruefully.

"Seriously, though, I am proud to command this fine Group and I am proud of every man here."

That would usually be very nice, I thought, *but today I'll bet we'd all rather be getting some extra sleep.*

The Colonel went on: "Today we are taking a few minutes to provide important recognition for various members of our team. When you hear your name called, please step front and center before me."

Well, this should be interesting...

The Colonel consulted his list—

"Peters, Thomas J. !"

Huh? What? Me?

Jim Stafford caught my eye and motioned me to go forward.

In a state of total confusion and surprise, I marched up and stood at attention in front of the Colonel.

"Men," he said loudly for everyone to hear, "as you know, Second Lieutenant Peters flies as Red Flight leader for the 501st squadron. As you probably also know, Second Lieutenant Peters is the leading scorer in the 339th group with 12 confirmed aerial victories."

What? Me? I'm the leading scorer for the group? That can't be true!

The Colonel looked me in the eyes and began: "Lieutenant Peters, first, I take great pride in awarding you formal advancement, based upon your time in service, to the rank of First Lieutenant, United States Army Air Forces."

The Colonel stepped forward with Major Stafford at his side. Major Stafford undid the single gold bars on my collar and the Colonel replaced them with the single silver bar of a First Lieutenant.

The Colonel spoke again: "Lieutenant Peters has distinguished himself in his craft as a fighter pilot and he serves as an example to the rest of us. Because of his admirable leadership and his extraordinary achievement of accomplishing, to date, twelve aerial wins over a skilled and determined enemy, I am very proud to present you, Lieutenant Thomas J. Peters, with the Distinguished Flying Cross."

I was in shock! The DFC? For ME?!

The Colonel again approached me and this time he pinned the beautiful blue, white and red ribbon with the gold propeller hanging beneath it to my lapel.

"I'm proud of you, Lieutenant," the Colonel said as he shook my hand, "and I'm sure your friend Sarah will be proud too." I noted the twinkle in his eye.

I was still in shock, but I finally stammered "Thank you, Colonel."

Then Major Stafford shook my hand and said "Keep up the good work, Lucky. I'm proud to have you in the squadron."

I did an about face and returned to my place at the head of Red Flight. The guys were all grinning at me and I felt ten thousand feet tall.

The rest of the ceremony was a blur. Several of the guys were promoted and others were commended for various things, but I couldn't begin to tell you the details.

But, as they say, all good things must come to an end...

We were back in the air on Monday, June 19, providing escort for B-17s hitting airfields in the Bordeaux area of France. On the 20th, we escorted B-24s to Politz, in far-north Germany. The Luftwaffe responded with a relish. We were very busy trying to keep the mixed bag of 109s and 190s away from the bombers. I got one 109 while he was focusing on a bomber. The bomber's gunners were blazing away at him, but he was just out of their range, so I decided to risk getting shot down by the Americans and I lit out after him. It was one of my easier kills; he was too focused on the bomber and just kept flying along. I dropped in behind him, closed to about 100 yards and fired away. It didn't take long for my 'fifties to chew him up and he caught fire and dived for the ground. The rest of the 339th did great, with Major Stafford getting a 190 and a guy named Don Wilson from the 500th squadron getting two 109s. Good shooting!

The next day, June 21, was the beginning of a unique activity. This was the beginning of "Operation Frantic", which consisted of about 150 B-17s setting out from their bases in England, hitting targets deep in Germany, and continuing on to land in Russia! According to the reports we heard, the group was attacked by a large bunch of German fighters as they neared Russia and six bombers were lost. The report stated that 144 bombers landed at various bases in Russia successfully. However, that night, the Germans attacked one of those bases where 73 B-17s were located and destroyed 47 and severely damaged the rest. Hmmm—interesting plan but, I don't know... At least we weren't involved.

On that same day, though, we went with some B-17s to Berlin and the Germans came up again. The guys of the 500th squadron claimed five, but we didn't get any. More strafing on the way home, but nothing notable.

That evening, I managed to get a call through to Sarah and I learned she is doing O.K., but still having some pain. I told her about my promotion and decoration and she was thrilled.

We didn't fly on the 23rd, but on the 24th, we went with some B-17s to attack the Saumer bridge, which was damaged, but not destroyed. No enemy fighters, so we strafed again before going home.

The next day, as Pappy and the guys were getting the J-Bird ready for our next mission, they noticed that the engine was running really rough. They quickly learned that many of the other planes were having the same problem. Some investigating found that the fuel supply they were using was contaminated. As a result, the 501st sat out the next couple of days while the ground crews flushed out the fuel systems and changed all the sparkplugs.

On the 27th, we went to the Paris area and strafed trucks and trains. One road convoy we hit seemed pretty important: it consisted of fifteen trucks that seemed to be carrying supplies to the German soldiers further west. Both White and Red Flights went in and we tore it up pretty completely. An army can't fight without food and supplies, so I guess our efforts were worthwhile.

I don't want to bore you with endless reports of our activities in June and early July that just say "More of the same", but that's what we did. Instead, I'll skip forward to some interesting stuff.

On July 14, something momentous happened: on that day, the 55th Fighter Group converted from P-47s to P-51s which meant the majority of Eighth Air Force fighter groups were now flying Mustangs. The conversion of other groups continued until the end of the year by which time, there was only one P-47 Group left. The Mustang is quite an airplane!

On July 19, we escorted B-17s for an attack on a new target. We were increasingly attacking petroleum and chemical plants, which made sense to me. I had long thought our repeated attacks on railroad marshalling yards were a waste of effort. There were so many tracks in a freight yard that the Germans could easily patch up a couple of them and keep traffic rolling. Destroying intermediate lines, tunnels, and bridges was very effective, though. It seemed like tearing up airfields was a bit questionable, too. Destroying the airplanes, hangers, and shops was definitely worthwhile, but putting holes in the runways was useless. They'd just fill them back up and be flying a couple of hours. But now, if we could destroy their chemical and fuel supplies, the war would literally grind a halt. We'd witnessed a bit of that when we flew over some German tanks that had been trying to hurry to the Normandy beaches but had run out of gas. After that, they were easy meat for the fighter-bombers. (Well, so much for how I'd run the war! For some reason, General Eisenhower hadn't yet consulted me...)

At any rate, on July 19, we escorted some B-24s to western Germany to attack a chemical plant, and a plant making hydrogen peroxide. On this mission I downed a 109, making my fourteenth victory.

July 24 was the date of terrible mistake. Headquarters had decided to use the heavy bombers *tactically* instead of *strategically*. What this meant was the B-17s and B-24s would be used for close support of the ground troops. Much planning went into Operation Cobra, but not all the planning in the world could affect the European weather. On the 24th, the weather was clouded over, but the bombers took off anyway, ordered to saturate a small rectangle in front of the 30th Infantry Division. By the time headquarters realized the weather was socked in and the bombers would have to drop blindly, they tried to recall the heavies. Sadly, bombs had already begun to fall. Some of the bombs landed in our troops and many were killed or injured.

On the next day, the weather cleared and the attack was tried again, this time including extensive efforts to protect our soldiers. We provided overhead escort protection over the target area and the experience was amazing. More than 1500 heavy bombers and uncountable numbers of medium bombers and fight-bombers took part. I have never seen so many airplanes in the air at one time. The engine noise sounded like continuous thunder, even with my flying helmet on. Generally, the bombing results were good, although serious mistakes did happen and U.S. soldiers were again killed by American bombs.

The weather on the 26th and 27th was awful and nobody flew. On the 28th I saw the most astounding thing I had ever seen in the air. We escorted the bombers in an attack on the synthetic oil plant at Merseburg and the German fighters we saw didn't attack us, they just stayed off in the distance and showed off. That was strange until we realized what we were seeing. There were about a half-dozen fighters diving and zooming and rolling at exceptionally high speed, and they were JETS! It was like they were showing off as a way to warn us about how outclassed we would be against them. My note: they were FAST!

On the 29th we went with the bombers back to Merseburg, but this time there were bunches of German fighters. We lost seven bombers but our fighter claims totaled 21 Germans downed. We didn't see any more jets, but the fighters were vicious. Jim got one and Rustler claimed a probable. I shot at several, but couldn't claim anything. Then the weather turned bad for a couple of days. Pappy was happy to have some time to work over the J-Bird to get everything back in top shape.

The first few days in August found us again strafing ground targets in central and eastern France. On August 6, 1944, our mission changed my life.

IMPROVING MY FRENCH

August 6 was a big day for the Eighth Air Force; nearly 1200 bombers and over 700 fighters attacked various targets across France and Germany. We went with about 400 B-17s to Brandenburg where they encountered clear weather and they plastered several munitions factories. The Luftwaffe came up to play and play they did. This time, in addition the usual 109s and 190s, we encountered some ME-410s and even some JU-88s, which were usually used as night fighters. There were probably over a hundred German fighters and we tangled with them all over the sky. I led Jim onto a couple of JU-88s where I took the left one and he took the right one. The strangest thing happened—I approached from behind and to the left of my target, and Jim from behind and to the right of his. That must have confused the Germans because mine broke right and Jim's broke left, so they turned into each other and collided and both went down! I guess I get credit for number fifteen—maybe.

The rest of the fight was the usual swirling of airplanes all over the sky. The enemy tried to get past us and attack the bombers, and some did, and we eventually lost eleven bombers, but we fighters claimed nineteen enemy shot down.

On the way home, we still had some ammo left, so Major Stafford allowed each flight to detach and search for "targets of opportunity". I led Red Flight back to the now-familiar area around Troyes to see if there was any rail traffic we could attack. The area around Troyes is flat farmland, so it was easy to see that nothing was moving around there. Then I led us up the river and as we approached Romilly-sur-Seine I spotted a freight train just leaving the large freight yard towards Paris. I guess I was careless because, rather than survey the scene before attacking, I just dove down on the train, coming in from the rear. Because it's so flat, they could easily see me coming. Just as I squeezed my trigger, Reb yelled "Look out!" The other three fighters pulled up and away, but I was too late. In the middle of the train was what we learned the Germans called a "flakwagon" and it had popped up and had me dead in its sights. I immediately started taking hits, but all I could do was keep flying at it and firing all the time. My 'fifties were chewing lots of pieces off of the gun mount, but I wasn't stopping their murderous fire. Even as I passed over, they trained around remarkable quickly and kept hitting me as I ducked low and tried to fly away. I turned north away from the rail line and my heart must have been beating a million miles an hour—I certainly never intended to get into a duel with a flak gun!

My relief when the hammering finally stopped was short-lived. As I tried to pull up to join the others I suddenly knew the J-Bird was in serious trouble. I could barely control the airplane and it certainly did not want to climb. The engine was screaming, but I wasn't gaining speed. A quick look at my instruments showed the temperature gauge off the clock, my airspeed was dropping like a rock, and I was just mushing along trying to even hold my already low altitude.

This is NOT good! I thought.

It was quickly obvious that I would not be merrily flying back to Fowlmere, so I got on the radio.

"Red Leader aircraft is severely damaged. I'm going to try for a bit more altitude so I can jump."

Jim answered, "Roger, Red Leader. You are smoking badly—get out of there!"

I would have loved to "get out of there" as Jim suggested, but I was still too low to give my parachute time to open. I had to climb—somehow. I had considered a belly landing out in one of the farm fields, but I knew the Germans held this area and I wouldn't have anywhere to hide if I slid to a halt in someone's turnip patch. Besides, I'd already bellied in once and it wasn't fun.

I tried adjusting the throttle, but as soon as I eased it off, the engine coughed and almost quit! I shoved the throttle full forward and the engine resumed its awful screaming. I tried to gently ease the stick back but the airplane buffeted so badly I thought it would stall—and a stall this low would certainly kill me. In desperation I tried rocking from side to side to see if that might somehow help. For some strange reason, it did help a little. At that moment, a beautiful P-51 came slowly along side of me—it was Jim!

On the radio: "Lucky, can you open your canopy?"

I tried it and, thankfully, it opened enough so I would be able to get out when the time was right.

Jim continued; "Your elevator is almost completely destroyed and most of it is hanging down in your slipstream, especially the right side. Your right aileron is shredded and your fuselage looks like a mangled tin can. When you rocked a minute ago, it seemed like the left side of the elevator caught a little of the airflow. Try that again and ease the stick back slightly."

I did, and the plane crept up a bit until my roll went too far and the plane started to slip off to the right.

"Lucky, try it again, but don't roll so far. Just roll a little and climb, then back to level, then roll again. Does that make sense?"

"Roger, Red Two."

So that's what I did. I don't suppose the engineers at North American Aviation would ever have approved but the trick helped a little and I could gain some altitude bit by bit. I was so frantic for altitude that I'd have flapped my arms if it would have helped!

But all good things must come to an end. I had managed to gain a couple hundred feet, but that was all the J-Bird could give me. The screaming engine was smoking and smelled terrible when, suddenly, it quit. It didn't even windmill—it just stopped. Time was up!

I tipped the nose down slightly to get airflow over whatever ailerons I still had and rolled the plane on its back. I had already released all my straps, wires, etc., so I just curled into a ball and dropped out.

In the movies, the hero always bails out and then counts to 10 before pulling his ripcord. I didn't have time for that—I just dropped and yanked.

Surprisingly, for such a flat farming area, I was above a wooded area with scattered small clearings. That observation was academic at the moment—I was praying for a big white mushroom to open above me. My 'chute streamed out and stretched upward, but I was falling like a rock. The good, green earth of France was coming up awfully fast! Then, suddenly, there was a fearful jerk that about took my breath away and the chute opened. Just in time, too, for I only had a couple of hundred feet to the ground. You are supposed to be able to "fly" a parachute in the direction you want, but I didn't have time to try. I just held on and hoped I wouldn't land in a tree. I also hoped I wouldn't land in the midst of a bunch of Germans. Actually, I just hoped!

Sometimes hopes—or prayers—come true. Mine did. I just missed the tree line and plopped down on the edge of a small grassy meadow. I hit much harder than I expected but I remembered something about cushioning the landing by bending your legs to absorb the shock. That didn't work. I crashed down to earth with all the grace of a falling flour sack and ended up on my face in the sweet green grass.

Well, I thought, *if I can smell the grass I must still be alive.*

I tried to roll over slowly to determine if I'd broken anything, and nothing seemed to hurt, so I sat up and unfastened my chute. I also tried to start breathing again—that landing was a doozy!

At that moment, I heard a beautiful sound—the music made by three P-51s flying by low and slow. The guys were still there and were checking on me—and maybe protecting me, too. What a great bunch of friends!

I stood and waved that I was O.K. Jim wagged his wings and they disappeared over the trees.

Welcome to France! I thought with a smile. *Welcome to occupied France!*

I began to gather up my chute. My plan was to gather the chute, hide it in the woods, and then hide ME in the woods until I could figure out where I was. I knew I had flown northward away from the rail line, but I had been so focused on keeping flying I hadn't paid attention to what I flew over. With so much farmland all around, I was actually glad I had made it to some forest. I figured it would be a whole lot easier to hide in the forest rather than some farmer's lettuce patch.

I was on my knees trying to quickly gather up the shroud lines and chute when I heard a noise from the woods. My heart about stopped!

I hope that's a deer or something!

I worked even faster, thinking I could run for cover if I had to.

Just as I was standing, getting ready to run, three figures appeared at the forest edge. They certainly saw me, and if they were Germans, my running would be useless. I tried to see if they were in uniform and it looked more like they were farmers or woodsmen or something. One of them stepped to the edge of the clearing where I could see him plainly.

"Monsieur!" He called quietly and motioned urgently for me to come to him.

I started toward him.

"Monsieur! Vite! Vite!"

He seemed to want me to hurry up, so I jogged to him. One of his compatriots grabbed the chute from me and took off into the forest.

The fellow who called me motioned me to be quiet with the universal sign of index finger across the lips. Then he turned and motioned me to follow him. The other man with him joined us and we started off deeper into the trees.

Well, I thought, *at least they aren't German soldiers.*

I supposed they might be taking me to the Germans, but my instinct was that they weren't. Otherwise, why the need for quiet?

We moved quickly, but quietly along the forest floor carpeted with leaves. After about ten minutes, the leader stopped us and motioned urgently for silence. The other man leaned towards me and whispered in my ear: "Les Boches! La!" He pointed to our left. Now I was scared—they didn't appear to be collaborators planning on turning me in, but being that close to German soldiers was

201

unnerving. The leader motioned we should hide behind a tree, so I lined up along one just to my left. I could hear voices nearby and the sound of heavy footfalls.

This is NOT the time to sneeze, I ruminated.

The sound of the footfalls and voices passed beyond us and I started to move away from the tree when the leader whispered "Hist!" and signaled me to stay still. Sure enough, along came more members of what must be a patrol. Soon, they, too, passed. We waited a few moments to be sure they were gone, and then continued quietly on our way.

After a hike of what I guessed was about half an hour, we approached another clearing. The leader stopped us and sent his partner ahead to reconnoiter. All was well, so we angled across the small grassy area and back into woods. This time it was just a few minutes before we suddenly turned to our right and clambered down a shallow draw surrounded by the forest. At the bottom, we went right again and moved quickly along until the draw shallowed out and we reached the edge of the forest and the beginning of a well-worn trail heading across the farmland. The leader motioned us to stop, still slightly back in the trees. He then came to me.

"Attends ici", he said, and pointed that I should stay put.

I nodded "yes" and slipped back into the trees. He and his partner set out along the trail that looked to me like a cow path back home on the ranch.

I checked my watch and noted it was about 12:30 P.M. I knew from our flights over France that it didn't get dark around here until almost nine. Because I knew there were Germans in the area, I certainly didn't expect to go strolling casually into some nearby town, so I guessed I'd be hiding in the forest for several hours.

Much to my surprise, about 15 minutes later, a young girl came looking for me. I stepped to where she could see me.

"Monsieur, parlez-vous francais?"

I knew what that meant: "No," I answered, shaking my head.

Then, with a very heavy French accent that I won't try to write she said "Oh, well I will speak English, then."

I smiled in relief. She must have been about twelve or thirteen years old, with a scarf wrapped about her head and very blue eyes. She had a bundle under her arm.

"There are Germans nearby and we must hide you quickly. Everyone saw your airplane crash and your parachute come down. Your other airplanes flew around you, so everyone knows where you are. Put on these clothes, quickly!"

I did as she said, but I wasn't happy giving up my nice clean flight suit and leather jacket in order to wear these filthy rags. I guess they made me look like a French farmer though—maybe?

"Give me your watch!"

This struck me as a strange way of stealing my expensive watch and I hesitated in giving it to her.

"Monsieur, they will know you are American by your wristwatch. Give it to me, quickly!"

What she said made sense, so I gave it to her—quickly!

"In a few minutes, my brother will come along here with our hay wagon. As he passes slowly, you must quickly slip out of the woods and bury yourself in the hay in the back of the wagon. Do you understand?"

"Yes, but won't the Germans search the wagon"?

She smiled a cute 'young-girl' smile, "Yes, Monsieur, but they will not find you. Good bye!" With that she left, hurrying off in a different direction from the cow path.

Even though the Germans were looking for me and even though they knew where to look, I was quite fascinated by what was happening to me. The men helping me, the young girl helping me, the brother coming to me help me—what a fascinating experience! And her comment "they won't find you"—what did that mean?

I wondered, of course, what would happen to me. Under the circumstances, I fully expected to be caught by the Germans. Then what? Probably a prison camp—unless they just shot me. In any case, it wasn't a pleasant future to contemplate.

While I waited, my thoughts turned, of course, to Sarah. How would she react to my being shot down behind enemy lines? She was mostly healed from her injuries in June, and we had spoken on the telephone a few days ago, and everything seemed so normal. Now this. It just made me more determined to make it back alive.

DODGING DEATH

London, in the summer of 1944, was again suffering at the hands of the enemy. The "doodlebugs", or "buzz bombs", or "the V-1", as they had now become known, were one of Hitler's "vengeance weapons". And they were falling on London at an alarming rate. The antiaircraft gunners were having the best luck bringing them down but, interestingly, the gunners in the heart of the city were soon directed to stop shooting at them because they were causing them to crash into populated areas. The RAF had made various attempts to stop them, even including pilots flying alongside and tipping their wings to throw off its guidance system, but shooting them down was still difficult. In fact, an average of 75 to 100 were hitting London every day, and on August 3, 104 flying bombs hit the city, killing hundreds!

Sarah's flat was a bit north of where most of the V-1s landed, but her office was within the danger zone. She and her co-workers were very sensitive to the fact that they worked on the eighth floor and when a buzz bomb came over, there wasn't enough warning to rush to the basement shelter. Their response was typical of the amazingly practical Londoners—they kept a couple of office windows open so they could hear one coming and then be able to duck under their desks! There had been some close calls that landed several blocks away, but they'd been lucky so far.

Sarah was at her desk, editing copy for a piece to be placed in all the London newspapers that discussed ideas for what to do if a buzz bomb came over while a person was in the street and no shelters were nearby. As she paused in her work and rocked back in her chair, it got Sarah to thinking about Tom.

He's flying in the war and his life seems to have become a bit safer as the German fighters have diminished, and my life in the city has become more dangerous because of these flying bombs. How ironic!

That got her thinking of the future.

I'm actually beginning to think there might be a future. The Allies are starting to advance across France and the Germans are dropping back. I've even heard some American soldiers talking about being home by Christmas. She smiled to herself. *And, yes, I want that future to include Tom Peters. Wonderful, gentlemanly Tommy!*

With a shake of her head, Sarah leaned forward and began focusing on her work. Any editorial changes she made always included her initials and the date. As she finished this one, she added "SB-6.08.44". (The English put the day, then month, then year as opposed to how Americans do it.)

Following lunch, Sarah enjoyed a meeting with Mr. Wooster that lasted about 30 minutes. When she arrived back at her desk, Louise, one of the typists, dropped in to discuss the piece she was working on. Sarah enjoyed meeting with "her girls" because they were bright and creative and their talks together were always fun and challenging. Later, Sarah was back to concentrating on her own pile of documents.

Maybe I'll be able to leave by six or so... She hoped. It didn't work, though, for, although the others usually left between 4:30 and 5:00, she usually stayed much later to keep up. Tonight it was getting closer to 7:00.

Sarah was deep in concentration when there was a gentle tap on her door and the door opened.

She looked up, rather annoyed, wondering who could be bothering her at this hour. She was amazed to see Pappy standing in her doorway.

"Pappy", she exclaimed happily, "What are you..."

Her voice trailed off when she saw the stricken look on Pappy's face.

"Oh, God! No!" She felt faint.

"Sarah, He's alive!" Pappy blurted. "He was shot down over France but he's alive! The other guys saw him wave."

Pappy rushed to Sarah who seemed about to collapse.

"Sarah, he's alive. He wasn't injured. The other guys clearly saw him parachute out and land in a clearing. They saw him up and moving around and he waved to them. Sarah, he's alive!"

As Sarah began to regain her breath, she looked into Pappy's sincere, frightened, concerned eyes and she began sobbing. "I - can't - lose - another - one!" she gasped between sobs. And then she cried and cried.

Pappy's composure wasn't all that solid, either. He'd been frantic when Lucky didn't come back, and when the others landed and Jim told him briefly what happened, he felt like the ground dropped beneath him. Once he got the whole story after debriefing, he got permission to rush to London. As he told Colonel Martinson, "That girl will NOT learn this by a telegram or telephone call. I'LL tell her myself!" The Colonel knew how special Sarah was to Tom and, actually, their romance had become something special to the entire group. Sarah had become something of a mascot to 501st, so Pappy got his jeep.

* * * * * *

Meanwhile, back in "La Belle France", my life became very interesting—emphasis on "very"!

As the young girl had said, soon a hay wagon came along, passing slowly along the edge of the woods and rocking slightly as it dropped through the gentle depression. To my surprise, it suddenly stopped right in front of me. I waited until the appropriate moment and then sprinted out and tried to dive into the wagon beneath the hay.

"Monsieur!" "Monsieur!" The driver was now standing on the other side of the wagon near the right rear wheel and was softly calling me. I had just dived into the hay, so I poked my head up and he shook his head "no" and motioned me out of the wagon. He joined me beside the right rear wheel. He nodded his head to the edge of the field just ahead of us where, to my horror, I saw the German patrol emerging from the woods.

It looked like I was caught. But then I had a sudden crazy idea: I motioned to the Frenchman to act like we were fixing the wheel. Then I motioned for him to begin forking in more hay and I would climb up and drive the wagon. His expression of questioning surprise would have been funny if not for the circumstances. But, come on, I grew up on a ranch—I can drive a wagon!

So that's what we did. Sure enough, the leader of the patrol and one of the soldiers came over, looking very suspicious. I decided my best plan was to play deaf and dumb, so when the leader spoke to me, I just stayed deadpan and ignored him. My Frenchman caught on and thumped on the side of the wagon pretending to get my attention. I looked around at him and he motioned to me about the Germans wanting to talk to us. I muttered some noises in my throat, hoping they would realize I was dumb and couldn't speak. Then the German began questioning my Frenchman. I speak neither French nor German, but I could guess what was being said. The German was loudly demanding to know where the pilot was and the Frenchman was answering just as loudly that he didn't know anything about a pilot. I just sat there, looking bored, and I tried not to let on that I was listening. While the shouting match was going on, a German Army truck came bouncing slowly across the field to pick up the patrol and the driver must have been impatient because he tooted the horn and motioned the leader to hurry up and get aboard. The rest of the patrol climbed in, but our two seemed determined to find the elusive pilot. While the leader continued haranguing the farmer, the soldier sidled up and leaned on the wagon beneath my high seat. He caught my eye and said something in a wry tone about the argument and chuckled, while watching me carefully. It almost worked—I nearly smiled at the ridiculous argument—but I caught myself and stayed dumb and deadpan. Soon, the honking became insistent and the Germans reluctantly gave up and went over and climbed aboard. As the truck drove slowly away, my Frenchman thumped hard against the wagon body and motioned for me (he called me "Rene") to get moving. We kept up our little pantomime until the Germans were completely out of sight.

That was a terrifying experience and I was just thankful that the Germans had somewhere else to go. Whew!

Under the circumstances, it made sense for me to remain driving the wagon, so my Frenchman, who introduced himself as Luc (it sounds like "Luke"), climbed up beside me and directed me over hill and dale to a farmhouse and barn out on the edge of the fields. We drove the wagon into the barn and, after unhitching the big, stolid cart-horse, we stood together. Luc looked like he was bursting with something, so I asked/mimed "What?" He burst into laughter and mimicked me making gurgling noises and playing dumb. We both laughed and he slapped me on the shoulder in good cheer. He then led me up a ladder into the hay loft where I was directed to stay put and hide. He left, still chuckling.

So there I was, snug in a hayloft in occupied France with German soldiers all around—Mama, I'm a LONG ways from Kingfisher, Oklahoma!

I must have dozed off, because it was dark when I heard a voice quietly calling "Pilote! Eh, Pilote!" I looked carefully over the edge of the loft and there was a middle-aged woman calling me. It turned out she brought me some bread and a thick slice of cheese to eat. I was famished and gobbled them down. She smiled at my wolfish behavior and left. A few minutes later, the young girl I'd met earlier came in accompanied by a man.

"Monsieur, this is my uncle. His name is Francois, and he will take you to people who can help you." Francois then spoke in rapid French to her. "He wants me to tell you that you were very lucky today. If the Germans were not pulling out of here and moving to the front, they would have caught you."

"Yes," I responded, "I realize I was very lucky, but we had to do something quickly, so we did our play-acting. I'm glad it worked!"

She giggled. "Oui. Luc is still laughing about your play-acting."

I was struck by how kind and helpful these simple farmers seemed to be. I know they could still turn me in and probably get a reward or something, but they didn't seem to be doing that.

Francois motioned for me to go with him. The girl stated as we passed, "Monsieur, be very careful and very quiet. The Germans are very terrible."

210

I nodded and smiled my thanks. Francois led me out past the farm buildings and across the small road out front. We started moving carefully along through the edge of the woods, our direction paralleling the road. We must have gone two or three miles when Francois stopped me and pointed to a community of lights in front of us.

"Bethon", he stated.

I suppose that's the name of the village ahead of us, I reasoned brilliantly.

He led us along the edge of the woods to where we found a small shack. I would have thought the shack was some abandoned tool house or something, but he approached it carefully and knocked some sort of coded knock at the door. There was a response from inside, so he opened the door and went in, motioning me to follow him. My curiosity was certainly aroused: would this be my betrayal to the Germans?

The inside of the shack was dimly lighted by a smoky lantern hanging from a beam running across the ceiling of the room. There was a person sitting against the far wall who spoke, with a heavy French accent:

"Well, Monsieur Americain Pilote, you have certainly stirred up the Bosch!"

I wasn't quite sure what to say to that—do I agree, or apologize?

He went on: "But you are a very lucky man. The patrol that almost caught you was their last quick try at capturing an American before the local garrison pulled out for the front."

"Well," I responded, "I'm certainly glad they left without me! And I really appreciate all the help I have received— but now I'm wondering how I can get back to England and to my squadron."

He laughed. "You Americans are all alike, you just cannot wait to return to the fray. But returning to the comforts of England is not as easy as purchasing a ticket on the next channel steamer."

I was a bit affronted by his condescension. "I know it isn't easy, and I certainly can't do it by myself. I appreciate all the help; I just want to get going."

I was startled by a voice from the shadows behind the door. "I say, old chap, don't get your dander up. We'll help you get back so you can win the war for us."

I turned and there, in the shadows, was a man sitting with his chair rocked back and his back against the wall.

"You're English!" I exclaimed.

"Right-O. We're all allies here—fighting to drive the Jerries out and all that." He then spoke to the two others in fluent French, apparently dismissing them. After they left, the Englishman rocked his chair to the floor and approached me with his hand outstretched. "Welcome to France, my American friend. We'll get you out, but you'll have to cooperate."

"Of course I'll cooperate. Sorry if I sounded a bit troublesome…"

"The first thing we'll do is figure out what to do with you. The scene is changing rapidly, so we have to change how we do things."

And so, sitting across from a total stranger who held my life in his hands, I began to learn of the French Resistance.

"To begin," he said, "although our local garrison seems to have pulled out, there are still hundreds of Germans all around us and they have become even more brutal than before. If you are captured, they will certainly kill the entire family that helped you, plus probably another fifty villagers as punishment. Their practice is to then burn the entire village to the ground."

Fear clutched my heart and I felt sick.

"But they wouldn't hurt that little girl…"

He grimaced. "Yes, they would with glee. Besides that 'little girl', as you call her is not so little. She watched as the Jerries murdered her grandparents along with other innocent civilians they simply pulled off the street in reprisal for a resistance attack. She serves as a messenger between the various resistance cells in this area and she has risked death on many occasions. She is aged fifteen years old, but she is as mature and collected as any woman twice her age. We call her 'Anne Marie'."

Hmm, I thought, *He said 'we call her', not 'her name is'. I'll bet none of the names I've heard are their real names.*

"My first advice to you is to not trust anyone. No matter how friendly they are, no matter how helpful they are, traitors are everywhere. Trust no one!"

I nodded. But I added: "Not even you?"

"No one!"

"Then why are you helping me?"

"Because that's one of my jobs." He paused thoughtfully. "Have you heard of the SOE?"

"No."

"The FFI?"

"No."

"The Maquis?"

"No."

He chuckled. "It's hard to remember that not everyone is steeped in this the way some of us are."

He continued, "My first act is to report to London that you are safe with me. What's your name?"

Well, I thought, *he said not to trust anyone...* I simply replied with my name, rank, and serial number.

"Very good. I'll report that on my next sked." (I learned that that meant his "next scheduled radio report.")

"For now," he said, "There will be somebody by to collect you. While it's still dark, you'll be taken to a hiding place. Don't do anything stupid, just stay out of sight. Events are happening as we speak that I think will affect us both in some major ways. You wait here until someone comes, and I'll be in touch."

With that he blew out the lamp and left and there I was— all alone in that small, dark, smoky shed. It was not a happy feeling.

It was about an hour later that there was a quiet tapping on the door. I held my breath and opened the door slightly.

Outside stood a grizzled little man who looked to be 90 years old and smelled like the inside of an ashtray. Whew, he reeked! He said nothing, simply turned as though he expected me to follow him—so I followed him. We walked along the road and right into town, but we stayed in the shadows and moved furtively. We passed a number of darkened buildings and, much to my fear, set a couple of dogs barking. In what seemed to be the center of town, we left the road and slid into a back alley behind the buildings that lined the road. We stopped at structure that looked to me just like all the others—in fact, it looked so old and broken down, I thought it was abandoned. He approached a weather beaten door in the rear wall and knocked softly twice. I was surprised that the door opened immediately, so I guess whoever it was must have been expecting us. He stepped aside and I went in. He left, having not said one word the entire time we were together. I passed through the door, which was closed immediately upon my entry. It was pitch dark inside, so I had no idea if I was with French people helping me, or the local Gestapo.

There was the scratch of a match and the pungent smell of a lamp being lighted. The feeble glow brought me relief—I shared the room with a woman, probably about my Mom's age, dressed in the worn clothing that seemed so common among the people I'd seen so far.

"Parlez-vous Francais?" She asked.

There was that question again. I really wished I'd taken French in school.

"No."

She motioned me to follow her, and I did, being as quiet as I could. We went through into another room, which appeared to be something of a kitchen, and then up a set of very creaky stairs. I tried to pick solid places to put my feet, but she motioned me to hurry and follow her. At the top was short corridor with a door off to each side, which I guessed to be bedrooms. At the end of hall was a cupboard door, sort of like a linen closet at home. To my amazement, she quietly opened the cupboard door and swung the set of shelves to one side. She motioned me forward and inside was a ladder-like affair reaching through a trap door into the attic. Using a crude sign language, she indicated I should climb up, pull the ladder up behind me, and go to sleep. So I did.

I awakened the next morning to a stream of weak daylight coming through the attic window. I almost went over to lean on the sill and look out to see where I was, but sanity caught up with me, so, instead, I very cautiously peeked out from the edge of the window, staying hidden behind the dirty cloth curtain and the window-edge.

I was looking down on the main street from my perch in the attic of a building set right in the center of a group of shops that lined both sides of the road. I realized that "my" building had a store in front of the living quarters I'd passed through last night. It was still barely light out, but there already was a horse-drawn cart passing slowly along the road, heading, I suppose to an outlying farm. It was so peaceful it was hard to realize that violent death was hovering nearby. It again struck me how evil were our opponents and how vital that we stop that evil.

The road curved slightly as it passed through town and I could see that Bethon was a very small town, truly a village. I didn't see any signs of Germans or a German outpost. I didn't know what else to do, so I just sat on the edge of the rather rickety cot I had slept on and awaited further developments.

I figured the sun had probably came up at about 6:30, so I wasn't too surprised when I soon heard increased activity on the street below as the town came to life. Then I heard a scratching sound from the cupboard below me. *So, I pondered, do I investigate, or ignore it?* I decided maybe they were trying to get my attention, since I had the ladder up in the attic with me.

I knelt down and lifted the hatch in the floor just enough to see below. What I saw caught my breath—not a 90 year old man who smells, not a motherly woman, but a rather startlingly attractive girl of about my own age was looking up impatiently. She saw me lift the lid and she spoke:

"Well," she demanded, "are you going to starve, or do you want something to eat?" This was said in clear English with a tinge of France mixed with England.

"Oh. I, uh…"

"Come on, let down the ladder, but be careful not to scrape the walls!"

216

I did as told.

'O.K, it's safe for you to come down for a few minutes if you stay in the kitchen to eat. I'll show you a hidey-hole in case anyone someone comes."

This was obviously a lady that knew what she was about and didn't brook any opposition. She carefully reconnoitered and led me downstairs to the kitchen. There I found the woman from the night before and man, dressed in slacks and an undershirt, eating breakfast from steaming bowls, and with a plate of obviously homemade bread in the center of the table.

"Sit here," I was ordered by the imperious young woman, "and eat quickly."

I was handed a bowl of porridge, something like thin oatmeal, which I dug into with gusto. The girl watched me carefully.

"You haven't been trained, have you?"

"Trained? Of course I've been trained! It took nearly a year to train me to fly fighters—what do you mean?"

"So you're not OSS?"

"I've never heard of the OSS," I stated firmly.

"It shows. You eat like an American, not a Frenchman. We'll have to teach you quickly or the way you eat will betray you."

I looked at her quizzically.

"Notice the way Papa (said 'pa-PA') holds his knife and fork: knife in left hand, fork in right hand, and he doesn't switch hands to eat. That is the common way here, and is opposite what you Americans do. That's the first thing the Germans look for."

That was startling, but made sense, so I then paid very close attention to how they held their silver, their cup, how they cut, and how they spread jam on the bread. This crash course in being a fugitive was hard work!

As I wolfed down my bowl of gruel and tore a large hunk off the bread, I looked to the girl and asked:

"So, what is your name?"

Her face turned hard and her eyes went cold. "Never ask that! Never!"

I was taken aback by her fierce response and I'm sure it showed.

She made a visible effort to regain her calm. "That's one of the important things you must learn—never ask names. If the Germans catch you and torture you for information, those names you divulge could kill us all!"

"Torture? I'd be a prisoner-of-war and there are rules about how to treat prisoners!"

She sneered. "Rules? There are no rules with our oppressors. You would be tortured until you told them everything. Then they would kill you anyway."

I definitely wasn't liking what I was hearing; but she seemed quite certain of what she was saying, and not as though she had simply heard a rumor. I believed her.

"You eat and then go back up. Don't go tromping about because we can hear every footstep, which means any Bosch who stops in could, too. You will be staying here for a couple of days while it is decided what to do with you. Be patient, be smart, and be quiet. We'll signal you by scratching like I did—ignore any other sound."

She looked at my empty bowl. "If you're finished, let's go." We went back upstairs and I climbed into my small dark home—or is it a prison?

218

That was the last time I left my room for the next three days. I learned that the small shop in the front of the building was a tobacconist run by "Papa". There was a trickle of customers including an old man who—hmmm—I wonder if he smells bad? Mostly I alternated between thinking of Sarah and thinking of a new J-Bird. I didn't see the girl again, just "Ma-MA" bringing me food, water, and carrying away my waste bucket.

Finally, at what seemed like the middle of the night of that third day in exile, there was a scratching from below. It's a good thing I was awake or I would have missed it. I cracked open the hatch and Mama was there beckoning me to come down. I did and she led me to the back door where I again met up with the smelly old man. Still wordlessly, he turned and started to go, so I followed. We reversed our previous course and ended up approaching the small shack in the woods. As we neared, he motioned me to slow down, and I heard the mumble of low voices apparently from a group just leaving the shack. Shockingly, I thought I recognized one of the voices giving sharp orders in French. The girl from where I was staying? I shook my head—no, it can't be.

A couple of minutes later, we resumed our stroll and again did the coded knock on the door. Entry was the same as last time, only this time there was just the Englishman.

"Well, Old Sod, it's time we talk. There have been momentous events afoot and they affect your immediate future."

I was, as they, "all ears."

He went on: "Usually, in a case like yours, we move you out of the area right away and eventually pass you along until you get out through Spain and into Portugal where you then can return to England. But things have changed. The Allies have broken out of the Normandy beaches and they are starting to move our way. Do you know of an American General named 'Pattern' or 'Patton' or something?

"I've heard of a General named Patton who was in trouble with the brass and ended up spending his time making speeches to woman's groups in England."

"Well, he's not making speeches anymore. He's in charge of the American Third Army; they landed south of Normandy and they are moving with incredible speed right toward us. Rather than send you all the way across France and Spain so you can get back to the Allies, I think we'll just keep you here and let the Allies come to you."

"Sounds good to me! But what about hiding me? I'm going stir-crazy in that dark attic room!"

He chuckled. "Yes, I'm sure you are. Well, the Jerries have been pulling out from this area and are headed to join the front lines well west of here. We have word that the several companies of motorized infantry that were based northeast of here will be passing through here early tomorrow on their way forward. Once they're gone, we might be able to allow you a bit more movement."

He stopped and seemed very thoughtful for a couple of minutes.

"Usually," he finally began, "I wouldn't divulge any information about our activities to you, but it has become less likely you will be bagged by the Jerries. Therefore, pay attention to what I tell you and, when you get back to London, make a point of telling this story to the highest ranking people you can find. You see, De Gaulle is twisting the story of the resistance to suit his own needs, but I think it's important that people know the true story of the bravery and devotion of these simple men and women. Most of the Allied leadership thinks we're a bunch of lunatics who just get in the way and they won't support us.

Others recognize our value and try to assist us with supplies and arms. Your General Patton and his Third Army are working very closely with us and the results are very successful."

Wow! That's a tall order for a simple airplane driver!

"I'll do my best."

"First, there is not just one 'Resistance', there are scores of different organizations and each has its own goals. Some want to be rid of the Germans, some want to be rid of the Germans and then take over the French government, and some just want to fight with each other over who is in charge. It is very confusing and sometimes very frustrating. After D-day, London finally let us shift to active attacks. Some groups, especially the Communists, had been attacking all along, but London didn't want a bunch of mayhem ahead of time making things worse. But now we all have the same orders: disrupt the German attempts to strengthen the front lines, and also disrupt their efforts to retreat to Germany. Our group is involved in all of that."

"Sounds like a Hollywood movie."

"It is far more serious than any silly movie. These efforts are helping win the war and will play a role in shaping the future of France and all of Europe."

"So—what are you doing here? You seem to be English and you are clearly in charge."

"Do you remember I asked you about the 'SOE'?"

I nodded.

"That stands for 'Special Operations Executive', which is one of the British agencies involved in intelligence gathering and sabotage. I am English, and I was trained by them and assigned here to organize, train, and equip the

Resistance cells in this area. I parachuted in here in March of this year."

I was intrigued.

He continued: "You also remember I asked you about the 'FFI' and the 'Maquis'? Those are two of the organizations I am coordinating. 'FFI' stands for 'Free French of the Interior' and the 'Maquis' are rural partisans grouped together in non-urban areas to harass the Germans. Our work has been hectic since D-day and my groups have been sabotaging German vehicles, destroying power line towers, and disrupting railway traffic." He chuckled, "They seem to especially enjoy blowing things up!"

"So, are they ex-military people?"

"Some are, but most are just patriotic people who want to get their country back."

I was awestruck to think of what these people were risking their lives and the lives of their families to accomplish.

"We have received reports that your Third Army just liberated Angers. Most of the German units from around here have moved west to counter them and that is where the motorized group is headed tomorrow. Our job now is two-fold: first, to impede their movement to the front and, second, to impede their retreat eastward as the Allies push them toward Germany. There are events happening tonight that should assist with those goals."

I thought about all he said and I reflected on my presence. "I feel so useless. Worse yet, I know I am a distraction for all of you that takes you away from the important things. I wish I could help..."

He smiled. "Well, my friend, if we need the services of a fighter pilot we'll be sure to call on you."

I was rueful at the prospect of not helping fight the war. I wanted to be back aloft in the newest version of the "J-Bird", dominating the skies. Or, if I was stuck here, I wished I could somehow take part. He read my mind:

"I appreciate your war-like spirit, but you aren't trained for this—sending you out would cause more trouble than it would be worth. Thanks, anyway. And now, I have an unusually busy night tonight; can you find your way back to the house alone?"

"Yes, I can find it, but what's the secret knock so they'll let me in?"

"Two short, sharp raps. And don't stand there knocking and knocking and knocking. Just once—they'll hear you."

And so I left. I was soon struck by how lonely and exposed I felt alone. I guess I had become comfortable with the presence of someone who knew what they doing—even if he was 90 years old and smelled!

I'M INCLUDED

I had been back in my luxurious digs for a couple of hours when, suddenly, far to the west there was a bright flash followed by a resounding "boom!"

Hmm. That must be one of the 'events' he mentioned.

And no sooner had I thought that when another flash appeared slightly more north from the first that resulted in another "boom!"

They sure are busy tonight!

I fell asleep thinking of Sarah.

The sky was just beginning to lighten when a noise from below woke me up. It sounded like someone closing one of the bedroom doors on the floor below. Hmm.

I hadn't gone back to sleep when, from the highway north of town I heard thunder. Not the thunder of a storm, but a noise that sounded like the motorcycles that always led the Fourth of July parade back home.

Ah, the German motorized units!

I slipped over by the window and peered around the edge. In moments, a group of three motorcycles with sidecars driving abreast swept around into town, followed by a long line of mottled gray-green armored vehicles, each with the swastika emblazoned on its side. As they passed, followed by a line of trucks crammed with troops, I wished I could call for some P-47s.

What a target! I thought.

A while later, Mama scratched and I was allowed to go down for breakfast. Everyone seemed unusually animated—I suppose because of the passage of the Germans. To my surprise, I was also allowed to remain in the kitchen while Mama washed the dishes. There was no sign of the girl.

As the morning wore on, Papa would occasionally poke his head in and report some new news to Mama. At one point, he smiled at me and made a "V-for-Victory" sign. I smiled back.

I was still downstairs when, in the mid-afternoon, footsteps sounded on the creaky stairs and "The Girl" came down. She looked like she needed more sleep.

So, I thought, *She must have been who I heard come in early this morning. I wonder what she was doing?*

She just nodded to me as she went to eat. I remained quietly in the corner.

After she finished her meager meal (ALL of the French people's meals were meager. I suppose the Germans got all the good stuff.), she looked over at me:

"What are you looking at?"

"You, of course."

"Why? Do you have romantic notions or something? Because if you do, forget it!"

That made me angry. "No, I don't have romantic notions! I'm in love with a wonderful girl in London. Besides, I learned a long time ago not to hug a porcupine!"

She thought about that for a second, then laughed. "I've read about your porcupine—is that what you think? That I'm all prickly?"

"All you've done since I arrived is bark and growl and order me around!"

She smiled. "You really don't know what a problem you are, do you?"

225

"Yes," I snapped, "I DO know what a problem I am and I don't like it any more than you do!"

She looked at me thoughtfully. Then she changed the subject abruptly.

"He wants to see you when he returns," she stated flatly.

"Huh? 'He' who?"

"Don't be dense! Woodman, of course."

"Woodman? Who in the world is 'Woodman'?"

"That's encouraging," she responded, "We really are getting better about keeping secrets. 'Woodman' is the Englishman you've been talking to. He is away for a few days, but he wants to see you when he returns. Just wait here patiently until then."

"How do you know all this?" I demanded.

She got that hard look in her eyes again. "I just know."

So I spent a couple of days hanging around in the kitchen, which was infinitely better than being crammed in the attic. And then there was the afternoon of "The Scare".

I was trying to help Mama bake bread when we heard increasingly loud voices from the storefront. The Girl had gone out a bit earlier, so I had no translator. As the voices grew in volume, Mama showed signs of fright on her face. She stopped her bread making and hustled me into the "hidey-hole" beneath the stairs. She had just closed the sliding panel when I heard the kitchen door slam open and a guttural German male voice loudly making demands. Papa was shouting, Mama was shouting, and the German was shouting. It also sounded like he was tearing the kitchen apart. Was he searching for me? I hoped I could be absolutely quiet.

My heart was pounding and my ears seemed especially sensitive. From the little French I was beginning to pick up,

226

it seemed he wanted something, but I couldn't figure out what. His voice came closer to my hiding place and I began thinking of what little I knew about how to fight someone. I certainly wouldn't go without a fight!

He seemed to pass on by me and he stopped at the cupboard next to the stairs. It sounded like he ripped the door off, and then I heard the sound of bottles clinking. "Ah,ha!" He roared. Then with more sounds of destruction, he seemed to leave the room and then the shop.

Mama and Papa talked angrily for a bit, then, as though she had forgotten me, Mama came and slid the panel aside and I emerged into a scene of devastation. Cupboard doors were jerked askew, pans and dishes and silver were strewn across the floor, and our bread dough was a dirty lump on the floor. Indeed, the cupboard door next to the stairs was ripped off and lying on the floor. No one appeared injured and, with a huge sigh of resignation, Mama began to pick up the mess, muttering something under her breath that was probably not complimentary to the Germans. Papa also took a deep breath and visibly calmed himself, then went back to the store out front.

Later, when The Girl returned, she heard the story from her parents and then explained to me.

"There was a staff car with three Germans in it and, apparently, one of them wanted tobacco. They stopped and one came in. Papa says he was drunk and he just grabbed a couple cans of tobacco. Then he saw the door into the house, so he pushed past Papa and burst in here. You heard what happened—after tearing the place apart, he found a couple bottles of wine and left."

I was so angry I couldn't speak. These fine people being treated so rudely really offended me.

In my anger, I asked; "Can you get me a gun? If anyone tries anything like that again, I'll shoot them!"

She laughed. "Down, Tiger! That would just cause a lot of innocent people to be killed and the village destroyed." She thought for a moment. "You really have been cooped up too long! Woodman is back and he'll come see you tonight. Be patient!"

The Englishman did come that night, and we sat in the kitchen alone and talked.

He filled me in: "The Americans are moving quickly and the Germans are falling back. I would estimate the advance elements of your Third Army will be near here by the end of the month."

I interrupted him: "Sorry, but I've lost track—what is today's date?"

"August 13. As I was saying, things are happening fast and my groups are especially needed at this moment, so we won't be around to help you. The Germans are falling back and they will certainly come back through here. Whether they will stay here to make a fight of it, or whether they will just pass through is anyone's guess. You're on your own, so be careful. Use your head. Stay in your room out of sight."

I nodded. *Another two weeks of being a prisoner upstairs,* I thought, *but I guess there's no choice.*

"Well, I have to go. I have to figure out how to blow a really big bridge to block the Jerries."

My ears picked up. "A bridge? You said a big bridge?"

He looked at me quizzically. "Yes, a big railway bridge. What do you know about bridges?"

I smiled smugly. "I graduated from college as an engineer. NOT a railroad engineer..."

228

He looked stunned. "So you know how a bridge is built?"

"Of course."

"So, would you know how to destroy one?"

"Sure. Enough well-placed explosive will bring down any bridge."

"And you would know how to place it?"

"Yes. I'm not an explosives expert, but I could show one where to place the charges."

He thought hard. "I may be crazy, but you may be just what we need. Come with me."

We went out the back door, down the alley and out onto the street. Instead of turning right to go to the shack, we turned left and strolled down the street. I tried to look especially French. We strolled along until we turned right onto a short street that ended at a barn-like structure. He carefully approached a door in the side near the rear and knocked the two-raps knock. The door opened and he carried on an earnest conversation with whoever was inside. He then stepped inside and motioned me to follow.

"This barn is where they store their crops . We sometimes use it as a rendezvous."

He motioned to a group of five other people in the room. "I believe you know some these fine people."

Two I didn't recognize, but one of the men was the old smelly man, one was the Frenchman who had been in the shack that first night, and one was—The Girl! I was shocked!

"What are you doing here?" I asked her in shocked surprise.

She glared at me. "I could ask you the same!"

"Now children," he soothed, "let's not fight!" He then spoke in French to explain to the others what I was doing there. The Girl looked at me speculatively.

He motioned me to his side, knelt, and rolled out on the floor a sketch of a cantilever railway bridge.

"This is our target. It is located about 20 kilometers away, near the town of Nogent-sur-Seine. It is a large steel bridge that carries two tracks across the Seine. It is a very busy and important line between Paris and Romilly-sur-Seine and Troyes. If we can destroy the bridge, it will block the Hun's retreat."

"What is your plan?"

"We're thinking we could place charges in the center of the bridge and blow out a section there. The entire thing should collapse after that."

I smiled and shook my head. "No, it won't. All you would do is blow out a section from the middle that the Germans could repair rather quickly. The bridge wouldn't collapse."

He looked at me doubtfully.

I continued. "This is a cantilever bridge. This type is built from both sides toward the center and is supported by this arch." I pointed to the gracefully curving arch that spanned the river. "The sides are self-supporting, so blowing out the middle won't drop the bridge."

The Girl translated for the others.

"So," he asked, "is it impossible to destroy it?"

"No, not at all, but it will take a fairly large amount of explosive. The fact that it is a double-track bridge makes it more difficult. The entire thing is wide and that adds strength. Do you know how many parallel support arches there are?"

The question was asked and different answers came back. "Deux." "Trois." "Quatre." Also some shrugged shoulders.

Great! Somewhere between two and four supporting arches.

"Obviously, two arches are easier to sever than three or four. We'll need to know for certain."

"So," the Englishman asked, "how do we go about destroying it?"

The others gathered around as I indicated on the sketch where to place the charges. "Charges here and here," I indicated just above the lower end of the arches near where they anchored to the cliff, "and here and here," pointing to the deck and arches above and slightly inside of the line where the lower ones were placed. "For good measure," I added, "blowing out the center section would be a good idea, too."

"So the number of charges depends upon how many arches there are?"

"Yes. If there are two arches, that would be two lower charges on each side of the bridge, two upper charges at the deck on each side, and two sets of charges to sever the track. Add another set for blowing the center. For two arches, probably—" I added them up, "twenty-four charges including the track."

After some translation, the Frenchman I had met in the shack exclaimed loudly "Impossible!"

The Englishman shook his head sadly. "Yes, I fear it is impossible. That bridge is heavily guarded and it would take a small of army of people all night to place all those charges. Just transporting that amount of explosive would be challenging."

I thought about it. "If there were enough people to have one charge per person, how long would it take for each person, simultaneously, to set his charge and run the detonator cord back to a central location?"

The Girl translated and then everyone engaged in a heated discussion, hands flying to demonstrate their points. Finally, the Englishman summarized:

"The slowest part is getting the people to the right place. Climbing all over that bridge takes time. And, if we have to ford the river to get to the other side, it will take much longer."

"But," I persisted, "what if they just ran across the bridge?"

"Well, best case, probably about thirty minutes. But that's impossible because of the guards."

I thought a bit. "So, is it necessary to completely destroy the bridge, or is it sufficient to blow out the middle? That will delay them but it won't stop them for long."

"Our orders are to destroy it, no later than the 20th, if possible. This is part of a concerted effort happening all along the river."

"Hmm. Is there any chance the Germans have already wired it for destruction for after they've crossed over?"

That evoked another round of animated conversation. Finally:

"We don't know. We can't get close enough to inspect it."

"Well, I'm certainly no expert in sabotage, but it seems like we need to know for certain how many arches, and whether the Germans have wired it. It sounds to me like we need a reconnaissance patrol."

So a patrol was planned—I was NOT included!

232

Two days later, the patrol returned. Four men had gone out and three returned; one was wearing a sling and one was bandaged. Things had gone well until a boat containing German guards patrolling the bridge from beneath came upon them. A fight ensued and our survivors were lucky to escape. Their report: two arches and no explosives in place, and guards at both ends and also in the boat beneath.

After another group discussion, it was decided to try to destroy the entire bridge, but to settle for blowing out the middle if that was all we could accomplish.

Preparations then went into high gear. The Maquis had already put a general plan in place earlier, so these detailed preparations went quickly. The Englishman arranged with other cells of his to assign their roles, caches of explosive charges were gathered, and a final assignment of the twenty-four "charge-placers" was done. I met with them and we assigned each specific person's placement.

The final plan was that assigned members would attack the German guards, hoping to eliminate them. The rest would place the charges as I directed. I would be on the scene to resolve any problems. We set out on the evening of the 18th to attack the bridge.

Obviously, we didn't gather thirty-some people together and march off to the bridge. People slipped away in one's, twos, and threes throughout the day. I went that evening with the Englishman, The Girl, and The Frenchman. Each of them were armed; The Girl carried a German rifle, no doubt "liberated" from a former member of the enemy army, and judging by the way she handled it, I had no doubt she knew how to use it.

BRIDGE OVER TROUBLED WATERS

We snuck out of Bethon and headed south and a little west through the woods. When we ran out of woods, we circled carefully around the town of Montgenost and snuck across the fields, also circling around Plessis-Barbuise and La Rue. We then entered a wooded band that took us all the way south to the Seine. Because of the way the river curves, though, we were far to the west of our target bridge and on the wrong side of the river. We had to cross the river because the bridge crossed the river west of us where the Seine flows north-south. Therefore, we had to cross the river where it flows east-west in order to circle around to reach the bridge. As a result, we crossed the river at Marnay-sur-Seine and, skirting the town, continued heading south and west. We crossed a canal and finally turned west and moved along the base of the railway embankment towards our bridge. Sound confusing? I'm sure glad I had the others as guides or I'd probably still be wandering around the French countryside!

The immediate area by the bridge was mostly fields, but there was a small area of woods right along the railway and we went in there. Soon after we entered the wooded area, we met up with several of the others. Consultations in French were conducted and final plans made. The Girl explained to me:

"It turns out the German movements to the front have helped us tonight. Instead of the usual large contingent of guards, there are only two on either side. We're not sure about the boat, but we have people placed along both river banks. We don't want to do any shooting if we can

234

help it because we don't want to alert the troops in town, so the boat is our big danger."

I looked to the sky and noted there were scattered clouds and bit of moon.

"Is it dark enough tonight?" I asked her.

"It will have to be. The guards changed about an hour ago, so we'll wait a while to let them become bored—and careless. Woodman will signal when to gather. After the guards are eliminated, one team will cross the bridge to work on the far side. Their wires will go to a detonator on that side. This side's wires will come here. On signal, the center team will be detonated first and we'll see what happens. As the center of the bridge falls, the other charges will be detonated and the entire bridge should go down—IF our consultant engineer has any idea what he's talking about..."

I just glared at her.

Time passes very slowly when you are hiding in a thin belt of woods from patrolling enemy guards. No singing, no whistling, no friendly arguments—just absolute silence. Five minutes feels like an eternity and an hour seems endless. But finally, the time was judged to be right.

The Englishman came and tapped me on the sleeve, motioning me to follow him. The Girl followed me. We slipped to the edge of the railway embankment near the bank of the river where we could see both the river and the bridge.

The Englishman whispered in my ear: "You stay here and supervise the placement and she will relay any instructions you have. Stay under cover until the guards are eliminated, and watch out for the boat guards!"

I nodded and he disappeared.

I looked at the bridge and I was stunned by what I saw. I had envisioned a graceful arch bridge soaring high above a gaping chasm. This wasn't that at all! It was about a hundred feet long and rather flat; it cleared the river surface by not much more than thirty feet. Why they went to the trouble to build a cantilever steel bridge here was beyond me—but there it was. I suppose they wanted a clear channel so river barges could pass or something.

We stood, hidden in the brush, listening carefully and watching the bridge. At one point we heard some rustling from the embankment above us and a couple of thuds. I guessed maybe that was the guards being knocked out. I glanced at The Girl and she smiled and made a cutthroat motion. Then I realized the guards weren't just knocked out.

Suddenly, there was a flurry of activity and many people rushed out onto the bridge. Some went to the other side, some stopped in the middle, and some stayed near us. People started climbing down the girders, clustering around the deck and rails, and a couple of brave souls were actually hanging from the center to attach their charges. I knew I was supposed to be making sure everyone was doing their job correctly, but I needn't have worried. A spectator would thought these people did this every night—they all were in just the right places.

We'd been at it about twenty minutes and some of the "placers" were already finished and off the bridge. Suddenly, from just upriver came a whispered cry: "Bateau! Bateau!"

The Girl whispered in my ear, "The boat is coming!"

That was the worst news we could have had! Suddenly, everyone on and about the bridge added extra haste to finish their placement and get off. They nearly made it,

236

too. But the last three, struggling to climb the girders to reach the deck and run off just weren't fast enough.

German voices cried out, so we knew the workers had been spotted. Then, moments later, there was a surprising splash and cries of fear from the direction of the boat. I leaned out a bit was dumbfounded to see that the resistance men watching the river hadn't just sat comfortably on the riverbank, but had actually floated out to where the boat would have to float by. They judged it perfectly and when the boat came within reach, they neatly tipped it over, dumping the Germans into the water. There were bubbling cries and struggles and, suddenly, silence. The boat sank slowly beneath the surface and there were no more signs of the Germans. But there were signs of the four resistance men waving their arms in triumph.

The Girl and I clambered up onto the embankment where we joined the Englishmen and probably about half of our team. The rest were doubtless on the other side. We were well back from the edge of the bridge and the Englishman signaled across to determine if everyone was clear. A welcoming wave signaled that all was ready.

The Englishman raised his arm and paused, then dropped it. Everyone waited with bated breath to see what would happen. There was a series of sharp "cracks!" from the center of the span. Smoke spiraled upward in the calm night air and, then, almost in slow motion, the center section of the bridge dropped neatly into the river waters below. Cheers broke out from both sides of the river.

He again signaled and we again waited. From the lower arches, just above the river, came simultaneous deep-throated "Booms!". A fraction of a second later came more "booms!" from the upper arches and deck. All eyes were on the bridge. It appeared nothing had happened—

the two sides of the span remained where they were. Then, a slight motion from the one on our side, followed by an increasing screaming of torn steel and collapsing metal. From across the river, a sudden drop and that entire side fell cleanly into the river. Our side twisted as it fell and ended up in a jumbled mass of bent and broken girders, the placid waters of the Seine flowing gently around them.

Vocal mayhem broke out. The cheering was so loud the Germans probably heard it all the way in Nogent-sur-Seine. But I was impressed again at the discipline of these fighters—they celebrated for a moment, then suddenly went silent and disappeared. It was time to get away before the Germans came.

* * * * *

The leadership team met again the next night, this time at the shack—I was included.

The Englishman spoke: "Well, my friends, we accomplished something vitally important last night. Our success was only one of several all along the river. Seven bridges were destroyed by our forces last night and that effort has funneled the Germans to the few remaining crossings. That will allow the Americans to concentrate on them rather than having to chase scattered groups all over the countryside. The Jerries are virtually trapped against the river and they will almost have to swim to get across. Congratulations to all!"

There were smiles and handshakes of gladness.

"And," he continued, "We have another one to thank—our American pilot certainly knows how to knock down a bridge! Thank you, my friend!" We shook hands in a firm grasp. The Girl smiled shyly and came to my side. She very chastely kissed my cheek. "Good job, American!"

I blushed.

"And yet more good news," the Englishman continued, "the Germans are so busy meeting the attack of the American army, they do not have time to mount reprisals for the destruction of the bridges." That brought murmurs of relief.

"Finally," he said, "we must still be alert because the Germans will most certainly pass this way again. They will be retreating, and they will be frightened, and that will make them especially dangerous. Lie low for now. We have much more to do before this war is over. As I learn more of the status, I will summon you."

I went back to my "lodgings" with Mama, Papa, and The Girl.

WALLS COME DOWN

The next night, I was up in my attic room when there was a scratching from below.

Hmm. Who could that be at this hour?

I lifted the hatch and there was The Girl.

"Could I talk with you?" She asked.

"Of course. Up here or down there?"

"I'll come up—lower the ladder."

I followed orders and, soon, there she was, sitting on the edge of my cot.

"First," she began, "I want to congratulate you about the bridge. I actually thought you were just being a boastful American, but you really DID know what you were doing."

I chuckled. "I was just thinking about that. My very first bridge as an engineer is one I destroyed!"

She smiled. "You know, the Americans are coming very soon and you will be rejoining them."

I nodded.

"The circumstances here will change drastically when that happens, and I was thinking it might be nice to—talk—to get acquainted. I know you refer to me as "The Girl", but I really do have a name."

"I'm sure you do, but if you tell me a name, will it be your real name, or your resistance name?"

"How about both? My 'resistance name', as you call it, is 'Jane'. I took it from your Calamity Jane who was such a good shot."

I laughed. "Not a bad choice!"

"I have not shared this with anyone since joining the resistance, but my real name is Marguerite."

"And as you know," I responded, "mine is Tom."

We shook hands.

My curiosity was aroused. "So, Marguerite, how do you speak such good English? Or is it that you speak good French?"

She smiled another lovely smile. "I am completely French, born and raised in this very house."

"Then, your excellent English?"

"My Mother has a cousin who married an Englishman. I spent many summers with them in England. And, if you're interested, I also manage a workable bit of German."

The conversation went on and I learned she had been a student at the Sorbonne in Paris, majoring in history. (Little did she expect to end up MAKING history!) In 1940, when the Germans marched into Paris, she hoped to continue her studies, but the invaders made that more and more difficult. Life became much harder under the brutal repression and then something happened that altered her life. In her words:

"I was still trying to study, but I was realizing it was becoming impossible. My boyfriend had finally quit school all together and he started getting involved passing out underground newspapers. We talked a lot about how we might help drive the Germans out, but I wasn't really involved. Then, one day, we had just parted and he was passing along the Rue Sugar handing out papers when the Gestapo caught him. He resisted and they shot him on the spot. At that moment, I sought out ways to join the Resistance."

It seemed like no matter where I was, London, Cambridge, rural France, the story was always the same: brutal treatment of innocent people. It just made my hatred of the evil even deeper.

We sat there in that tiny darkened attic sharing about our pre-war lives. I told her about Oklahoma and she told me about growing up in Bethon. Then I had a question:

"Marguerite, you said that after the Americans come through, life will change dramatically for you. That makes sense, but how will it change? You will be free again and can pick up your life. Isn't that exciting for you?"

Her response surprised me.

"Yes, it is exciting, but it is sad as well. The men of the Resistance will join in alongside of your soldiers and will continue the fight to drive the Germans completely out of France. I will not, for there is no room for women in your army. Going back to school will not be possible for quite some time because so many of the Professors have been deported and killed. Instead, I will remain here at home and assist my parents. And perhaps I can find some way to help our town begin to function normally again. My contribution to the war will be over."

She sounded wistful, and it gave me a lot to think about.

I was keeping track of the date by now, and August 23 was a big day. In the mid-morning, we heard vehicle noises coming towards us from the south. My heart leapt to think my countrymen were finally here—but I was soon disappointed. I hastened out of sight and up into my attic perch where I could see out over the town. There, curving through town came tanks, trucks, and infantry—but NOT Americans. We witnessed a scruffy, thrown-together collection of Germans heading disconsolately north and eastward toward Germany. They looked tired and their usually spotless equipment and vehicles were dirty and worn looking. Some even appeared to have suffered battle damage. Apparently, the Americans were hot on their heels and that brought me hope.

More joy rang out on the morning of August 26: reports were confirmed that Paris had been liberated on the twenty-fifth! Shouts of "Paris Libre"! rang throughout Bethon and there was literally dancing the streets.

Late in the evening of August 26, three of us met with the Englishman and he reported what he had just learned from his radio contacts in London. We learned that late that day, Third Army's Twentieth Corps forces had liberated Nogent-sur-Seine (the site of our recent bridge success) and also Troyes.

"Well, Tom, the Englishman said, "I rather suspect we'll be seeing some Americans early tomorrow."

I couldn't help but smile.

"We'll need to determine how to return you safely to your compatriots—it wouldn't do for them to think you are a German and shoot you!"

Hmm, good point!

"In addition, we'll be joining with your forces and I would like to get a couple of my men with the leaders of whatever force first shows up to act as liason with them. I'll send two of them to meet you at the house at 5:45 tomorrow morning. Then see if you can flag down your troops and meet with their commander."

Indeed, just before sunup on August 27, 1944, two resistance fighters showed up at the house. Each of them spoke heavily accented English, but we actually spoke little. Our ears were turned to the south, straining to hear the oncoming American forces. We were not disappointed.

Soon after sunrise, the unmistakable noise of advancing mechanized troops came to us. Who would they be? German? Or American?

Our first clue was the outbreak of boisterous cheering from the far side of town. At last, the moment I had dreamed of for nearly a month occurred. The beautiful sight of an American M-4 tank rumbling around the curve and coming toward us, followed by other tanks, trucks, light artillery, and good 'ole American troops! The population of Bethon flooded the road, cheering, waving, and trying to touch hands with the liberators. It was a wonderful thing to witness the end of more than four years of brutal repression and watch as freedom broke forth. But I wasn't just a spectator!

I stepped out to the edge of the crowd and as that first tank clanked noisily past, I shouted up to the tank commander.

"Hey! I'm an American pilot! You just liberated me!"

He lifted his headphones.

"What did you say? I can't hear you!"

By now I was running alongside the tank and shouting.

"I'm an American pilot and you just liberated me! Who should I talk to?"

"Tell the guys in the jeep!" And they rolled majestically away, tank after tank after tank.

The citizens were delirious—and I was worried. What if I couldn't connect with the troops and they just drove away, leaving me here?

Behind the tanks came numerous "army trucks" filled with troops. I shouted to everyone I saw:

"Hey, guys! I'm an American pilot. Get me out of here!"

I received lots of greetings and a few laughs, but no help. After the trucks, there was brief gap in the line of vehicles. Then my best chance appeared—a jeep with three guys in it.

I ran out and stood resolutely in the middle of the road waving my arms, hoping they would stop—and not run over me or shoot me.

"Hey, guys! Stop! I'm an American pilot and you just liberated me. Help me!"

The driver hesitated, then pulled over and stopped. I ran to them.

"Hey, buddy, what did you say?"

"I'm an American pilot. The resistance protected me until you guys finally got here. Help me get back to England and my squadron. Please!"

The passenger gave an order to the man in the rear: "Get the Colonel on the horn and tell him we just found a guy who says he's an American pilot who needs help. See what he wants us to do."

A brief radio conversation took place, and then the radioman stopped talking and looked at me.

"The Colonel says to ask you your name and serial number."

"Peters, Thomas J. USA , T-843177."

He repeated it into the radio. He received an answer and looked at me.

"O.K., the Colonel says for you to wait here and he'll send a jeep to get you. They'll confirm your identity at headquarters."

The passenger, a sergeant, barked: "O.K! Let's get this show on the road!" And away they roared in a cloud of exhaust.

My French compatriots and I waited impatiently for over an hour when, at last, a jeep with a driver and an MP came slowly along the road.

I again stepped out. "Hey, guys! I'm the pilot!"

They pulled over. "Get in!"

"Gladly!" I responded. "But these two men are resistance fighters and they are supposed to hook up with you fellows. They know who the Germans are, where the Germans are, and how many Germans there are. They need to come, too."

The MP looked distinctly unhappy. After giving the situation some thought, he made a decision:

"O.K, all of you get in, but if you try any funny business, I'll shoot first and ask questions later!"

The driver turned the jeep and headed back the way they'd come. As we passed my home of the last month, Marguerite was standing in the door to the shop. She waved a small wave—I waved back, and then we went around the curve and headed out of Bethon.

THE ARMY WAY

Colonel Horace C. Albritton was sitting in the shade of a tree at his desk,—an upended ammunition crate—trying to keep track of his rapidly advancing troops. As if that weren't enough, there now stood before him a scruffy looking character who claimed to be an American fighter pilot that Albritton's troops had just liberated from some French village. Albritton was awaiting the response to a radio message he'd sent more than thirty minutes earlier, attempting to verify this fellow's identity. Meanwhile, he had called his intelligence officer and dumped the two Frenchmen on him.

Who knows, he thought to himself, *maybe they really can help us catch up to the Germans.*

The Colonel's orderly came breathlessly to him.

"Sir, here's the answer to your message about the pilot. It says he's real, but to ask him some personal questions that only the real guy would know." He handed over the message sheet.

"Stanislawski, " the Colonel barked irritably, "how many times have I told you to just deliver the messages, not read and comment on them?"

"Yes, sir!" The orderly slipped away.

I waited expectantly for the "personal questions".

"O.K., fly-boy, what were you flying when the Luftwaffe shot you down?"

My turn to be irritable.

"I was shot down by a flak wagon in a train," I snarled. "I was flying a P-51 named the 'J-Bird'."

"Where are you from?"

"Oklahoma. A ranch near Kingfisher."

"Who won the '40 World series?"

That was easy; I am an avid baseball fan. "The Cincinnati Reds won the '40 Series."

"O.K, so you really seem to be Peters, Thomas J. Why don't you have your dog tags?"

I was incredulous at the stupidity of that question. "Because I was hiding from the Germans and tried to pass as a Frenchman. Those dog tags would have killed me!"

"Oh. Yeah, I suppose."

He looked at some papers on his desk. "O.K Peters, here's what we're going to do. There will be a truck leaving soon carrying wounded men back to Normandy for evacuation. You'll go with them. From there, you should be able to end up back in England. The truck's over there." He pointed to a truck being loaded with litters of wounded men. "Good luck!"

*　*　*　*　*　*

In addition to the normal hectic routine of keeping the planes of the 501st flying, Pappy had been haunting Colonel Martinson for any news about Tom. The latest was the surprising report that Tom had been instrumental in destroying a critical railway bridge, and he had dutifully reported that to Sarah. Pappy was worried about Sarah, though; her normal upbeat response to Pappy's calls was beginning to sound listless. With the onset of bad flying weather at the end of August, Pappy decided to go to London to see Sarah and find out what was wrong.

As usual, Sarah was at her desk when Mrs. Breese announced that Pappy was there to see her. She had come to think of Pappy as almost a second father and was always happy to see his weathered face peeking around the edge of her office door.

248

"Hi, Kid! Can I come in?"

"Pappy, you rascal, you always manage to show up at the just the right moment. I'm especially happy to you. Of course, come in and sit down."

Then it dawned on Sarah that Pappy's visit might not be such good news.

"Oh, Lord, Pappy, not more bad news! Please, no more bad news!"

He quickly reassured her. "Oh, not that Sarah! I'm sorry if my coming has scared you! No, I came just to see you."

Sarah smiled in relief. Then her natural sense of humor kicked in: "Why, Pappy, are you courting me?"

The poor man's flustered response made her laugh. "Pappy, you jewel, I'm just kidding! So why ARE you here?"

He drew a deep breath. "Sarah, you're like a daughter to me and I worry about you. Lately on the 'phone, you don't seem yourself. I don't hear your usual sparkle, so I came to find out what's wrong and see if I can fix it."

Sarah was touched and Pappy noticed it.

"Sarah," he continued, "I'm not trying to pry. But you know I'm a mechanic and mechanics fix things. How can I fix whatever's bothering you?"

She rose from behind her desk and, as Pappy stood confusedly, she went around to wrap him in a big hug. He hugged her back, and there they stood.

"Oh, Pappy, I hate this war! I'm so worried about Tom! Blowing up bridges with the resistance? He's crazy!"

It slowly came to the edge of Sarah's notice that the usual noise from the typists outside her office had gone silent.

249

Suddenly, the door opened unannounced and there stood a fellow with long, rumpled hair, an unkempt beard and worn, dirty clothes. He also smelled bad.

Sarah bridled. "How dare you burst in here like that! Who—"

And then it dawned on her who this dirty, smelly creature was.

"TOM!"

*   *   *   *   *

As I passed through the typist office, the girls suddenly went silent. Then one of them shrieked in recognition, and I shushed her. I approached Sarah's door and the moment I had dreamed of the entire time I was in France was before me. I opened the door without knocking.

Imagine my surprise when I opened the door and found Sarah wrapped in the arms of—Pappy!

She stared to snap at me when she suddenly figured out who this awful looking character was.

"TOM!" She yelped and rushed at me like a football linebacker. She almost knocked me over.

I couldn't hold her tight enough; she was crying and I was crying. And then I looked over her shoulder at Pappy, and he was crying.

And then pandemonium broke loose. All of the girls started cheering and yelling and clapping—even Mrs. Breese! At that moment, I was in the only place in the world I wanted to be. I was home—with Sarah.

*   *   *   *   *

Unfortunately, the air force wasn't as concerned about my love life as I was. Pappy used Sarah's telephone to notify

Colonel Martinson of my return and the Colonel said I should report back to him. But I had also been directed to report to the SOE office in London, and also to report to 8th Fighter Command in Bushey Hall, wherever that was! Now that I was back with Sarah, all I desperately wanted was a long, hot shower, a razor, and a haircut.

Sarah thought, though, because I was already in London, I should contact SOE and find out what they wanted. That was a mistake. Again using Sarah's office telephone, after a long wrangle about security with the telephone operator, we were finally given a number. I called them and was told to report immediately to a certain address. They meant RIGHT NOW! Rats! No shower yet.

Since Pappy had a jeep, and Sarah knew where the address was, the three musketeers climbed into the jeep and away we went. Sarah and Pappy waited downstairs while I was escorted upstairs to a very plain office where I was directed to wait. Finally, an officious little man with very little hair and big, horn-rimmed glasses came in and told me they had received the reports from France about my bridge escapade and they wanted the entire story. They wanted it transcribed, so I waited some more until a secretary came in and I told the entire story from the beginning. At the end, the little man asked me an interesting question. He had been telling me that SOE wanted to find someone from France to serve in the London office as a central person to communicate with the resistance units now attached to various army commands. He asked if I knew anyone who might do. I immediately thought of Marguerite, who still wanted to serve her country. I gave what information I had about her and, at long last, left.

It was too late to see anyone else that day, so we went to Sarah's flat where I enjoyed a lingering bath with mostly hot water. Pappy went out and found me a razor and so, after a long month, I was finally on the road to being clean. We spent the night at Sarah's, but we were rudely awakened early the next morning by pounding and shouting at the door. It was Jim, Reb, and Rustler doing their best to waken everyone in that part of London! What a reunion! In addition to bringing me all the latest squadron news, they brought my complete uniform—great guys!

Sarah knew of a barber nearby, so, late in the morning, the whole troop tramped down to the barber. After a quick cut, I was at last back in military shape. We decided that, after lunch, we would all make the trip to fighter headquarters. And so we did—two jeeps worth with Sarah as navigator. It turned out Bushey Hall was far to the northwest of London on the way to Oxford, so we had a fun ride despite the wet, gray weather.

I reported in to a desk in the front lobby of the beautiful building—I later learned it had once been a golf country club. The other guys, Pappy included, couldn't resist seeing what our headquarters looked like, so they came in, too. The WAAF behind the desk chuckled at our group but, after consulting a list, addressed me.

"Lieutenant Peters, you are to meet with Lt. Colonel Young to be debriefed about your recent experiences. As for these other men—and lady—I'm not sure what to do. We're not exactly a tour stop. I'll see what I can do, but first, I'll call Colonel Young and tell him you've arrived."

When she got off the telephone, Reb sidled up to the desk. "Ma'am" (said in two syllables: 'maa-um'), do y'all have a boyfriend (bowy-frey-und)? Cause this-here country-boy thinks y'all's mighty cute" Followed by the cheesiest, "I'm an angel" smile ever given.

We all broke out in hilarious laughter and the poor WAAF blushed three different colors.

"I, uh, I mean," she spluttered, "I…"

She was saved by an officer striding around the corner—a GENERAL officer!

"Oh!" She composed herself, "General Kepner!"

"So what's going on out here and who are these people," he demanded.

We all popped to attention and saluted. I guessed that as the former leader of Red Flight, I should speak up.

"Good Morning, General! Peters, Thomas J, First Lieutenant, 501st Fighter Squadron, 336th Fighter Group!"

"Are these people with you, Lieutenant?

Oh, boy, I thought, *is my goose ever cooked!*

"Yes, sir! I was directed to report here upon my return from France, and these people are from my squadron. Oh, and may I introduce Miss Sarah Brockman?"

The General graciously greeted Sarah, "Miss Brockman. Lieutenant, your name rings a bell. Why, again, are you here?"

"Sir, I was shot down behind enemy lines in occupied France about a month ago. I was liberated by our advancing troops a couple of days ago and I have just returned to England. I understand I am to be debriefed here."

"Ah, that's it. You're the first to come back to us directly without going all through Spain and Portugal and we want to learn all you can tell us. Welcome home! Don't I also remember something about decorations recently and goodly number of kills?"

Now it was my turn to be embarrassed. *Holy cow! They've heard of me here?*

"Well, yes, General, I was decorated shortly before I went down and, I think I have fourteen confirmed victories."

Another officer had walked up beside the General and he spoke.

"General, if this Lieutenant Peters, he has fifteen confirmed kills."

Jim couldn't keep quiet. "General, Lieutenant Peters is our flight leader from Red Flight and we watched him go down. Having him back alive is a great thrill for us!"

"Pretty good flight leader, is he?" The General asked.

The others answered in unison, "YES, SIR!" Reb piped up in his southern drawl, "General, we love this guy! Besides, he's the only one in the squadron that can understand me!"

We all enjoyed a good laugh at that. The General then took the time to shake each of our hands and thank us for our good work. He smiled at Sarah and left. We were thrilled to meet and shake hands with the commanding general of the entire Eighth Air Force fighter command. What an honor!

The rest of the afternoon was long. I went with Colonel Young to tell my story and the others ended up getting a brief guided tour of the offices where they met several others of our high-ranking leaders. Then they waited in the lobby.

Colonel Young impressed me as a very sharp individual. All through my story, he'd interrupt me with very incisive questions about my experience. He was especially interested in my bridge escapade. There was a secretary present to again take it all down.

"So, you took it upon yourself to join in destroying the bridge?"

That sounded like maybe he was unhappy I had gone.

"Yes, Sir. Their original plan would not have accomplished what London ordered them to do. In fact, it would hardly have slowed the German retreat at all. I was able to use my engineering background to assist them and I went along to be sure they placed the charges correctly."

He nodded, and went on to other topics. We finally finished very late that afternoon. As we were wrapping things up, he said something that concerned me greatly:

"O.K, Lieutenant, we're finished here and I thank you for sharing your story. Now, as a 'Returned POW', you are entitled to a week's leave. Am I correct in assuming you'd like to spend it in London with Miss Brockman?"

Returned POW? That didn't sound right.

 "Well, yes, Colonel, I'd love to have a week in London with Sarah but, sir, I'm not a 'Returned POW. I was never a captive—I spent the entire time with the French resistance, so I guess I'm more like a liberated pilot."

He frowned. "Hmm, I see. I'm not sure that makes a difference—wait here while I check on something." He left the room.

He returned a few minutes later. "Well, your official status is 'Liberated Aircrew', but you still get the week leave."

I couldn't have smiled any bigger. "Yes, Sir!"

"I'M GOING WHERE?"

That week with Sarah was a real eye opener for me. We were in Sarah's flat and it started with a comment I made...

"Sarah, you seem really tired. Is everything O.K.?"

To my shock, she started crying gently.

"Tom, I'm exhausted. I can barely get through each day and there's no end in sight."

"Have you talked to your boss? Maybe they can get someone to help you catch up."

That brought a wan smile.

"No, Tom, it's not tired from work—it's tired from life. The war just goes on and on and the buzz bombs keep coming, and the city is just a huge pile of rubble, and there's no food, and there's no clothing, and there's..." She broke down in sobs.

I held her, trying to somehow infuse her with good cheer—or at least better cheer. It got me to thinking about what life in London must be like on a daily basis, and that made me realize I really hadn't paid much attention.

She sighed and tried to compose herself. "I'm sorry, Tom, I'm not very good company right now."

I held her tight.

"Sarah," I said quietly, "I just realized how little I know of what you deal with every day."

"I know, Tom. You live on your base and you eat good food and you have hot water, and you have a warm place to sleep. Then you come to town and we spend our time together and you have money to spend and you are cheerful and fun. It's so disconnected…"

I chuckled. "Sarah, I don't know that I'd describe Red's meals for us as 'good food'!"

"Oh, but they are! Whether it's as good as what you had at home isn't the point. You get nutritious meals that keep you well-fed. We don't. Our food supply is very limited and very tightly rationed. You throw away more meat in a day than we see in a month!"

She paused thoughtfully.

"Tom, when you arrived here yesterday, you took that long bath and commented that it was 'mostly hot'. That 'mostly hot' bath used up the last of our coal ration for the month, so I'll be taking cold baths for the next few days. And that razor Pappy brought back…?"

I nodded.

"…because Pappy doesn't have any ration coupons, and because razors and razor blades are strictly rationed, the only way he could buy the razor and blade was through the black market."

I was stunned. "The black market? For a razor?!"

She nodded ruefully.

"Sarah, I had no idea! I feel so bad…"

"I don't want you to feel bad, but I want you to understand."

She smiled a shy smile.

"You know these underpants I'm wearing?"

I nodded.

"These are the only good ones I have and I save them for special times. I wear them, then wash them overnight and

257

wear them again the next day. For work and normal times, I wear my old ones, but they are simply a collection of mends held together by more mends. And Tom, I'm doing better than most everyone else in London. I have a good-paying job, I have a private flat to live in, and I can manage to get the essentials I need. Many others can't do that. You have certainly noticed the piles of rubble all around the city and all the bombed out buildings? Those were homes for tens of thousands of people. When a doodlebug lands and destroys an entire block of housing, the people who survive the blast have nowhere else to live. There's nowhere to go!"

I felt sick in the pit of my stomach.

"Tom, you have probably noticed that you Americans are viewed here with mixed feelings. There is a great deal of resentment that your country happily stayed out of the war and sold us all the supplies we could pay for. Then our money ran out. If your President Roosevelt hadn't dreamed up 'lend-lease', we wouldn't be able to keep fighting, AND we'd starve. We appreciate the help, but we resent being bankrupted by our closest ally. And then you got dragged into the war and, suddenly, all of you well-fed, well paid, happy soldiers flooded our country. Our men are off fighting all over the globe and, while they're gone, you happy-go-lucky fellows with money in your pocket scooped up all of the girls and show them fun like they've never dreamed of. Think of that..."

That last part really scared me.

"Uh, Sarah, are you telling me that, uh, maybe you, uh, don't want to see me anymore?"

"Oh, no, Tom! That's not what I mean! No, I just want you to realize why we don't always fall at your feet in thanks."

I thought about that.

"Sarah, I don't think any of us expect anyone to 'fall at our feet in thanks'. We just want to get this war over with as soon as possible. We're here to help fight the Nazis and bring an end to this horrible mess. I joined because I want to help. I recognize the horror of it all and my time in France made it even more clear to me; that's what I want to help stop. As far as the boy-girl thing, it's certainly not fair, but it seems like that was bound to happen. But Sarah, you've not only shamed me, you have also frightened me. What about us?"

I held my breath in fear of what she'd say.

"Oh, Tom, you poor boy! I've been so hard on you today! Tom, listen carefully: I have fallen completely in love with one of those dear, confused and confusing Americans. Tom, I love you! Completely! Don't ever fear for my love. Oh, my poor darling!"

And it was her turn to hold me tight. Whew! My heart started beating again.

That first week of September, 1944 was amazing. We talked endlessly and I learned about life in London, and in England at large. And I told her everything I could think of about life in the U.S., especially life during the war. I told her about OUR rationing and how we had so much less to eat or wear because we sent so much of it to them. We both learned a lot about each other's lives and we came to see the strange balance between our countries. She was able to take occasional time off, so we traveled all through the city and she explained what had happened as she showed me the different areas and the unimaginable devastation. It changed me.

Something we came to notice was that the buzz-bombs had nearly stopped. That Thursday we read in The Times where one of their government officials wrote that the buzz bombs were, indeed, done, and that we'd won the "Battle of London". The next event was a shock.

The next evening, we were eating in Sarah's flat when, at about a quarter to seven in the evening, off in the distance there was a sudden Boom! Boom! It didn't sound like a V-1. I looked at Sarah and she looked at me. There was a new look of fear in her eyes that hadn't been there for the last several days.

"What was THAT?" I asked. Then: "Sarah?" I questioned.

"Oh. No! I think that was something we've been fearing. Because of the work we do, we have special information from the Ministry of Information. Hitler has been boasting and threatening about another, even worse 'terror weapon' and I think that must have been one. The intelligence reports are that it's a high-altitude rocket that can't be heard or seen. It just drops out of the sky with no warning. But we're pledged to secrecy, so please don't tell anyone—the government will announce it at the right time."

Indeed, we had just heard the first of what came to be called the "V-2."

* * * * * *

The following Monday, I reported back to Bushey Hall for assignment. I knew I couldn't just go back to leading Red Flight, so I wondered where I'd go.

Upon reporting, I was taken to the office of a Captain, who let me sit down. He scanned a list and found my name.

"Well, Lieutenant," he said, as he looked up smiling, "You get to home! You're being assigned as a combat tactics instructor right in your home state! Congratulations!"

I suppose I should have been thrilled, but I wasn't. I felt sick and angry and betrayed and I guess it showed on my face.

"Is that a problem, Lieutenant?"

I drew a deep breath to try to calm down.

"Yes, Sir, it is a huge problem in several ways. First, I'm a combat fighter pilot, and a pretty good one. That's what I signed up to do and that's what I still want to do. Second, I can contribute more to the war right here rather than teaching students back in Oklahoma. I'm here—they're not. Finally, I am about to be married to a wonderful English girl and I'm not leaving without her! I appreciate your efforts, Sir, but is there a way I can protest my assignment?"

He frowned and looked decidedly unhappy. He picked up the telephone on his desk and asked someone to bring him my file.

When the file arrived, he spent several minutes in deep concentration as he read through my information. He muttered as he read: "Hmm, flight leader." "Fifteen kills, eh?" "The DFC? Good job!" "Fought with the Resistance." "Well! Blew up a bridge!" "Liberated directly by our troops..." He finally came to the end.

"Lieutenant, you have had an interesting war. I'm going to take this to my higher-ups and discuss it with them. You go ahead and go back to wherever you're staying and come back here tomorrow morning at, say, 9:00 AM."

My Mama taught me to pray, and was it ever time to pray! I called Sarah at her office and told her what was going on and she told me to come there, so I did. She surprised me upon my arrival by having all of the office staff gathered in the typing room.

She led me to the front of the room.

"Ladies and Gentlemen, by now I think you all know Lieutenant Tom Peters of the American Air Force. He has no idea what I'm about to ask him to do, so let's be kind."

She turned to me. "Tom, is the story of the bridge considered classified?"

Huh?

"I guess not, at least, no one has said so. Uh—why, Sarah?"

"I would like you to tell that story to these people. It is interesting and I think they will find it inspiring to learn of what the Resistance is doing. Will you tell the story?"

Oh, my!

"Well," I answered hesitantly, "I'll try, but I'm not much of a public speaker!"

So I launched into the story, beginning with my being shot down and quickly giving them the overall scene. Then I went into more detail about the resistance group, giving due recognition to the English leader, 'Woodman', and then I told them about the bridge. To my surprise, the people actually seemed interested and I was encouraged by their attention. When I finished, they applauded!

That night, back at Sarah's flat, the discussion was all about my being sent home. I started by telling her that I wouldn't leave without her—if she'd go.

She was deeply thoughtful. Finally: "Tom, I love London and I love my country and the thought of leaving family and friends and moving to a strange country is terrifying." Another thoughtful pause: "But I realize our country, and especially this city, will never be the same again. It will take a long time to convert our economy back to producing civilian goods. I am convinced that all of the difficulties and deprivations we currently face will not end when Germany surrenders, but will go on for a long time—maybe years—before we're back to whatever 'normal' is then. We are bankrupt, so there won't be money to rebuild. Besides, as you've seen, the destruction is so total and so widespread, I expect it will take fifty years to build it all back up."

It was a bleak picture, but I thought she was probably right. Then she asked me a question that almost knocked me off my feet.

"Tom, is this discussion of my leaving England some strange way of asking me to marry you?"

I blushed.

"Well, no, I'm not that sneaky, Sarah."

So right there, with her sitting on the sofa with her feet curled beneath her, I knelt down on one knee before her and took her hands in mine. Her eyes got big.

"Sarah, I'm not that sneaky, or even that creative, so I'll say it straight out—Sarah Brockman, you are the most wonderful human being I have ever known. I love you more than I ever dreamed I could love anyone. Sarah, will you make my life complete—will you marry me?"

At that moment, time stood still for me. I knew that within the next few seconds, my entire future would be decided. I couldn't breathe and my hands were shaking.

Sarah looked deep into my eyes, and then her tears started flowing down her lovely cheeks.

"Yes, Thomas Peters, I will marry you with all the joy in my heart!"

I couldn't help it—"Yee, Haw!" burst from my lips.

* * * * *

The next morning, I reported back to Bushey Hall but I was surprised when I was directed to Colonel Young's office rather than to the personnel Captain I had talked to earlier. I knocked and was told to enter. I was surprised upon entering to see Colonel Young at his desk with Colonel Martinson at his right and Major Stafford at his left! They all looked very stern.

"Uh, Oh!"

I approached the desk and did my official 'reporting in' routine. There was no chair, so I remained standing.

Colonel Young spoke.

"Lieutenant Peters, you have formally requested a change in your assignment as it was explained to you yesterday, is that correct?"

"Yes. Sir. I ex..."

The Colonel put his hand up to stop me.

"Lieutenant, you will answer my questions directly and no further explanation is desired!"

"Oops!"

"You have given various reasons for requesting a review of your new orders. This is highly unusual and is not appreciated by everyone here at headquarters. Your orders were drafted with your skills and experience in mind. Your orders reflect the needs of the service and you are expected to comply with those orders. Do you understand this?"

"Oh, boy, am I in trouble!"

"I understand, sir."

The Colonel looked at papers on his desk, and then gave a quick glance to Martinson and to Stafford. It was quiet and I was feeling about as low as a worm. I highly respected and deeply liked these men and I was ashamed to have let them down. But I couldn't say anything.

Finally, Colonel Young looked up at me.

"Lieutenant Peters, your superior officers have explained your situation to me. They have stressed your excellent service and your record confirms that. We agree that you have much offer the Army Air Force and we fully intend to take advantage of your abilities."

"Oh, my. Look out 'yellow perils', here I come!"

"These fine officers have also explained your situation with Miss—Brockman, is it?"

I nodded.

"I am sure you will not be surprised to learn that you are not the only American to fall for an English girl. Unfortunately, not all of those situations involve a fine young woman such as yours and that is why the army makes it extremely difficult for army personnel to marry to indigenous civilians."

"Now I don't have a clue what he's leading up to!"

"Given the overall situation, it has been decided to make slight changes to your orders. But don't smile yet! You are still being transferred home, but with changes that will better utilize your skills."

"Uh, oh. If I know the army, I'm about to be sent to some Nowheresville supply depot to fly a desk. I should have kept my mouth shut!"

"Lieutenant, I can see from the look on your face that you are confused and chagrined. Don't be too hasty to judge!"

The other two cracked a smile.

"Lieutenant Thomas J. Peters, you are hereby ordered to Luke Field, Arizona, to serve as the squadron leader for a new fighter squadron that is forming for service in the Pacific Theater. You will form this squadron as quickly and thoroughly as possible. We may be about done here in Europe, but the Japs still need a licking!"

I couldn't breathe. A Squadron leader! I recalled what a great teacher and leader Major Stafford has been and I only hoped I could do as well. Holy, Cow! I couldn't have spoken if I'd had to. Then the three men stood and came to front of the desk.

"Lieutenant Peters, front and center!"

I popped to attention and moved forward to stand before Colonel Young.

"Lieutenant Peters, you were recently promoted to the rank of First Lieutenant. I'm sorry, but I must ask you to remove your bars from your uniform." He held out his hand.

"How can I be squadron leader if I get busted? Huh?"

I removed my bars and placed them in the Colonel's hand. He then turned to Jim Stafford.

"Major, would you take over, please?"

Major Stafford moved in front of me.

"Lucky, you've hit the jackpot!" Then, speaking formally: "Lieutenant Thomas J. Peters, USAA, in order for you to accomplish the duties you have been assigned, you are hereby advanced in rank to Captain, United States Army Air Force." He approached me pinned the twin silver bars of a Captain on my collar.

Jim held out his hand. "Congratulations, Captain!" If I'd shaken his hand any harder both our arms would have fallen off. I also shook hands with the other two officers, and then Colonel Martinson spoke.

"Lucky—I don't usually address my pilots by their nicknames, but yours seems especially appropriate—we have another issue to deal with. Usually, upon transfer back to the States, a man gets a month leave so he can visit his family and rest before taking up his new duties…"

I started to blurt out something, but his hand went up and stopped me.

"As a leader of men, Captain, you must learn that there is a time to speak and a time to be quiet." He smiled. "As I was saying, that is the usual procedure. Your situation, however, is a bit different. Each of us has met your young lady and we are very impressed with her. I have a question: have you asked her to marry you?"

I beamed. "Yes, sir!"

"And, apparently, she said 'yes'?"

"Yes, sir!"

"We thought that might be the case. In fact, a little birdie you call 'Pappy' reported that to us. As a result, Colonel Young has secured special permission for you to take your leave here in England instead. Would that be your desire?"

I almost jumped up and down. "Yes, sir! Most emphatically, sir!"

Martinson smiled. "That's settled, then. As you know, the process to marry her is a long one, but if you'll get your papers together and ready as quickly as possible, you submit them to me and I'll see what I can do to push them along."

What wonderful men! I want to be a leader like these guys. It'll be hard to leave them!

Colonel Young stated: "Peters, today is September 12. You report back here at 0800, October 12, packed and ready for transport."

I was able to obtain all of the needed forms and lists while I was there and, boy, was it a pile!

THIRTY DAYS HAS SEPTEMBER...

I was able to stay at Sarah's flat, even though she had to go to work nearly every day. I got started on my pile of paperwork and she also started on the stuff England required of her. This getting married is a whole lot harder than just saying "I do"!

She came home that first night and was all smiles.

"Well, look who's home," I greeted her, "and what a beautiful smile! I guess you're happy to see me?"

"Of course I'm happy to see you, my husband-to-be! But something happened today that makes me even happier."

I waited rather impatiently for the explanation.

"I was able to speak with both Mr. Smith and with Mr. Wooster to tell them our good news. I really didn't know what to expect because I know they count heavily on me for the success of our office. Tom, they were both as pleased as could be!"

"Hey, that's great, Sarah! I imagine it will be a huge loss to them when I scoop you up and carry you away."

She chuckled. "Yes. But there's more! We talked for most of the morning about what to do after I leave and we shared ideas about whether there might be someone who could replace me. Do you remember meeting Jane Humphries?"

I thought hard and the name seemed vaguely familiar, but I certainly couldn't say I remembered anything specific.

"We ran into her and a friend as we came out of the Charleston Grill one evening back before you were shot down."

"Hmmm. Maybe I do. The sirens started and we hurried away? She has short brown hair and glasses?"

"Yes! That's her! Jane and I competed for best marks in our writing classes at University. I mentioned her to my bosses and they told me to contact her and see if she might be interested or available."

"Wouldn't that be wonderful! When will you call her?"

Sarah smiled smugly. "I already did. She's very interested and she'll be here at about seven so we can discuss the position." She paused. "And I made another very important telephone call."

I waited for the other shoe to drop.

"Tom, there are a couple of very important people you need to meet. They will arrive here tomorrow afternoon."

"Who in the world?" I thought.

"Well?" She questioned.

"Uh, Sarah, I have no idea. I don't really suppose Winston Churchill and his wife are coming to dinner?"

She laughed. "No, silly! Besides, I mean someone REALLY important!"

I looked at her questioningly.

"My parents!"

Wow! That IS important! I had not met them, although Sarah told me a lot about them. This really is an important meeting—if they disapprove of me, my future will be terribly empty.

We whipped up some quick food and finished eating in time for Jane to arrive. While the girls talked, I sat at the table and filled in forms. I joined in some chit-chat at the end of their meeting and formed the impression that Jane, while not as amazing as Sarah, was interested and could be a viable replacement. But my thoughts were really on the following afternoon.

I was showered, scrubbed, shined, toothbrushed, and shaved in time for the expected arrival. Sarah was at work, leaving me alone with her parents so we could, as Sarah gleefully expressed it, "get acquainted". I was more nervous than the first time I faced an ME-109!

The dreaded/terrifying/anticipated moment arrived. At 1:15 precisely, Sarah's bell rang. I drew a deep breath and went to answer the door.

"Oh, boy, here goes!"

I opened the door and before me stood a couple. The man was tall and slender with perfectly combed silver/white hair and very distinguished looking. At his side stood what was essentially an older version of Sarah. Well dressed, carefully groomed and a very attractive older lady. What a beautiful couple! I was abashed.

"Well, " said the man in that beautiful English accent, "Judging by the uniform, you must be the wonderful American Lieu—oh, I'm sorry—CAPTAIN Peters that our daughter has told us about. Told us rather endlessly, actually"

"Yes, sir. Thomas Peters. I am very happy to meet you." We were standing awkwardly and I was overcome by nervousness.

"Son, perhaps you might invite us in? This hallway is a bit public..."

Add "embarrassed" to my list.

271

We went into the "living room", which was simply the area where Sarah had placed a couch and a couple of upholstered chairs, and sat.

Well, you dolt, I chided myself, *You're off to a lousy start! Buck up!*

Fortunately, as a Barrister (what Americans call a lawyer), Mr. Brockman was very well spoken and very organized in his thinking. That saved me!

He looked at me and chuckled. "I take it you are not accustomed to meeting your fiancé's parents?"

"Sir," I laughed, "I am so UN-accustomed to meeting my fiancé's parents I am speechless!"

Mrs. Brockman spoke gently: "I believe your name is Thomas? Is that how we should address you?"

Still smiling, I responded: "Yes, m'am, my name is Thomas, and you can call me that, or 'Tom'."

I finally started to relax and it was much easier to converse when I could actually breathe.

I had no exposure or experience with people from the English "upper classes" and I had no idea how to behave. Fortunately, Sarah's parents were not at all snobby but, instead, were warm and welcoming. They quickly put me at ease and we went on to spend the afternoon in very pleasant conversation. I knew I was being evaluated and, woven skillfully into the talk, were the expected questions about my background and especially how I planned to support their daughter in the future. I was ready for those, but I also realized how I had to stay on my toes when talking "casually" with a British lawyer!

Sarah arrived from work and we all went out to a wonderful dinner. (It was possible to find a wonderful dinner in London, IF you knew where to go and who to ask.) The talk was sparkling and ideas flew back and forth at lightning speed. I came to understand how Sarah had become the incredible woman she is. What a joyous evening!

Sarah took the next day off and the four of us spent a cozy morning continuing with our getting acquainted. Her parents planned to return home later that afternoon and, by now, I had come to like and admire them. What exceptional people!

During our talking, Mr. Brockman asked me a question I was totally unprepared for.

"Thomas," (he had adopted 'Thomas' as his preferred form of addressing me), "once all the permissions are received and you are married, how will Sarah travel to America? It's no longer as simple as just purchasing a steamer ticket."

"Mr. Brockman, frankly, I have no idea. I've been so focused on completing the paperwork I hadn't come to the transportation issue." I laughed, "if it was up to me, I'd jam her into a P-51 and fly her there myself!"

Mrs. Brockman smiled and said "That seems a bit cozy, doesn't it?"

Mr. Brockman commented, "I somehow doubt that such a direct approach would work." Turning to me, he continued: "Thomas, when we get home, I'll contact some friends and see what they might suggest."

I would accept any and all assistance with deep gratitude!

A bit later, we accompanied them to catch their train back to Westcliff-on-Sea. Just before they boarded, Mr. Brockman shook my hand and, with his wife and Sarah looking on, spoke seriously to me:

"Captain Thomas Peters of the United States of America, although the thought of our beloved only daughter living far across the sea is daunting, I want you to know that my wife and I can now understand why Sarah is so taken with you. You impress us as a fine young man; she truly loves you and it is obvious that you truly love her. We agree that you will be a fine son-in-law and we want you to know that you have our full permission to marry our daughter. We welcome you to our family!"

WOW! A thousand times WOW! Or should I say "Yee, Haw!"

PAPERS AND PARTIES

The next couple of weeks are a blur. We were turning in Sarah's papers to her government and also to ours so she could get the necessary visas. We were turning in my papers to Colonel Martinson so he could help us get the required Army approvals as soon as possible. And we were communicating with Sarah's father about transport for her. I hoped that BEING married would be a whole lot easier than GETTING married!

The first good news was that Sarah's father managed to get us a waiver to the required time for posting a marriage. Therefore, when everything else was in place, we could go directly to a local register office to have a civil marriage. The next good news was that Colonel Martinson had managed to push my paperwork through the Army channels and we got the required signatures in record time. Perhaps the biggest miracle was that the U.S. State Department approved our application and granted Sarah, in advance, a spouse's visa so she could join me in the U.S. following our ceremony. She would simply have to take in our official marriage certificate to prove we actually got married and they would activate her visa. Unbelievable! Thank you, U.S.A!

At that point, all that was left was to orchestrate the actual ceremony with all the necessary participants arranged. We each needed two witnesses, so I lined up Jim Stafford and Pappy. Sarah arranged for Effie and Jane. But then another wrinkle surfaced: Pappy announced that immediately following our wedding, we were REQUIRED to attend a combination wedding party/goodbye party at the 336th base in Fowlmere. He stressed that it was NOT optional! In the end, we decided that it would be easier to have the ceremony in the Register Office in Cambridge so Jim and Pappy could be there and Sarah's parents, Effie, and Jane could all join us there. What a great plan! Except it didn't turn out that way...

What happened was this: we had to set the date to be after we had all of the papers and permissions in place, but it obviously it had to be before October 12 when I had to leave. We also had to factor in the flying weather. We needed bad weather so Jim and Pappy could attend. (Strange, isn't it? We wanted BAD weather for our wedding day! Who'd of dreamed that?) After conversing with all involved parties, we set the magic day as Wednesday, October 4, 1944. That worked for everyone, so I thought all was well. Oops! Not quite!

We contacted the Register Office in Cambridge to make an appointment for the ceremony and were told, incidentally, that the office was small and there was room only for the bride, groom, and witnesses. That's a problem, and that problem got bigger with a call from Pappy.

"Lucky, I just found out that all of the guys from the 336th want to attend your wedding. Is there room?"

I about fainted. "Uh, Pappy, that's wonderful, but it's a huge problem. The office is too small to even have Sarah's parents attend. We've got a problem!"

Pappy was silent for a moment. "O.K, Lucky, don't sweat it. I'll make some other arrangements and call you back later. 'Bye."

I explained all this to Sarah and, to my surprise, she took it very calmly. When I commented on her equanimity, she replied:

"Tom, you, of all people, know Pappy and how he routinely accomplishes the unbelievable. If Pappy says he'll fix it, I believe him—he'll fix it!"

Late the next day, I was at Sarah's alone when the telephone rang. It was Pappy.

"O.K., Lucky, here's the plan: We'll have the wedding here in the mess hall. There's plenty of room for everyone and we can have the party here right afterward."

I was astounded, but I also knew Pappy didn't know how the English system works.

"Pappy, you're a magician, but it isn't that simple. The British requirements are very strict. How will we get the civil official to do the ceremony at the base? And how will we get him all the way out to the base? And how will we get clearance for all these civilians to come onto the base? And how will we...?"

"Lucky, hold on, boy! It's all worked out. I called the lady at that office in Cambridge you talked about and everything's all set with them. Then I worked with Colonel Martinson and he got clearance from headquarters to have everyone here, civilians included. The Colonel even wants to make a short speech, if they'll let him. We decided to have the ceremony at 1800 hours and the party will take the place of evening chow. Everybody here is excited. This'll be the most fun we've had in a long time! Red even said he'd bake a special cake!"

What can I say? If Pappy says he'll fix it, he'll fix it!

* * * * * *

October 4 was quite a day. Sarah and I, her Mom and Dad, and Effie and Jane, all piled into Sarah's dad's car and away we went to Fowlmere. We arrived in plenty of time and, when we reached the gate guards, we were told to wait. Soon a jeep came, containing the ever-present Pappy driving and Colonel Martinson riding with him. The Colonel got clearance for us and onto the base and over to the mess hall we went, to be met by Red, standing at the door. Once inside, we were amazed and very pleased to see the way the room had been decorated with colored streamers and balloons. Somehow, the "balloons" didn't look quite right but, oh, well. There was even a big banner reading "Congratulations Lucky and Sarah!" hanging on the back wall. In front of it stood a podium, I think from the briefing room. Then Red, beaming proudly, led us over to a table covered with food. In the center of the table was the largest cake I have ever seen; lettered on it in colorful letters was "Happy Marriage Sarah and Tom" and it had two P-51s crossing below it. I complimented Red on the cake and his response was classic:

"Well, I'm glad you like it, Lucky," he smiled broadly, "after all, us Oklahoma boys gotta show these others the right way to do things!" What a guy!

Beginning at about 5:30, there was a rush of people coming in. The squadron guys, the maintenance guys (looking especially scrubbed and clean), and many of the officers arrived and all the people quickly brought life and laughter to the old mess hall. Soon, to everyone's surprise, a bus pulled up out front and a herd of people got off and came in. It turns out Mr. Wooster and Mr. Smith managed to somehow come up with a bus to bring themselves and their entire staff out to Fowlmere. With that, the party began early. Everyone was talking and laughing and having a great time. I was enjoying watching how Sarah's "girls" were suddenly a huge hit with the men of the 336th. I think some serious romances might have begun right there in front of Red's cake! Almost lost in the chaos was a small man in a business suit and an older woman accompanying him. They found their way to Colonel Martinson who showed them to the podium. Our "Officiate" had arrived.

Pappy had found a PA system somewhere (I wonder what unit is suddenly missing its system?), so Colonel Martinson blew into the microphone, nearly deafening the rest of us. The Colonel spoke:

"Ladies and Gentlemen, I am pleased to introduce Mr. Buddingham from the Registry Office. He will be conducting the ceremony this evening, assisted by Miss Warrington."

A scattered few people applauded—probably the first and only time in his entire life that Mr. Buddingham had ever been applauded! The Colonel continued:

"Please take your seats, everyone. There should be plenty of seating at the tables. Please take your seats, now."

There was a noisy shuffling of feet and scraping of chairs, but eventually, everyone was sitting. Miss Warrington led me, Sarah, our witnesses, and Sarah's parents to the back of the room where she gave us some simple instructions.

Now that he had everyone's attention, Colonel Martinson launched into his "brief" speech:

"Ladies and gentlemen, this evening is a very special occasion in our unit. We will assist in the marriage of one of my fine pilots and his very wonderful lady. But first, I want to simply express my pride at being the leader of the men of the 336th Fighter Group. These men have performed far above what anyone expected of them—and I mean ALL these men! The pilots who, I am certain, are the best in the entire Army Air Force; the officers and leaders who make each mission possible; the support people who house and clothe and feed these people; and, certainly not least, the Crew Chiefs, Mechanics, Armorers and all the other specialists that stay up all night and often all day, too, to—as they say—"Keep 'em Flyin'! I am honored to serve with you men!"

Loud applause and cheers broke out, because, you know, WE'RE proud, too!

After a while, the Colonel got it reasonably quiet again. "And so, squadron mates and friends, we now turn to the marriage of Miss Sarah Brockman— Interrupted by loud cheers and wolf-whistles—and our compatriot Captain Thomas 'Lucky' Peters." More yelling and cheers that became a chant: "Luck-y!" "Luck-y!" "Luck-y!"

I looked at Sarah and saw we were both in tears.

The Colonel patiently motioned for quiet and, eventually, everyone settled down. What a wedding—and we weren't started yet!

The Colonel turned to Mr. Buddingham. "Sir, please proceed."

I hadn't paid much attention , but I vaguely remembered there was a beat-up piano in the corner of the mess hall. I surely noticed it now.

One of the mechanics sat down at the piano and looked over at the Colonel, who nodded. The mechanic began to play a rhythmic classical piece, and boy, could he play!

Miss Warrington nudged me, so I started up the center aisle, followed by Jim Stafford and Pappy. We reached the front, moved to the right of the podium, and turned to face the crowd. A couple more bars of that beautiful music and the pianist softened the song, and then stopped. A pause, and then he began the familiar strains of the Wedding March. I looked at Sarah and I have never seen a more radiant nor beautiful woman! Sarah's mother led the group and was followed by Effie and Jane. Sarah was escorted up the aisle by her father, who looked so proud and touched I thought he'd pop. My emotions were so overwhelmed I don't know words to describe how I felt.

I had learned that a civil ceremony in England could not contain anything of a religious nature, and that the official conducting the marriage had tightly proscribed duties that were limited to the official act of marriage. In fact, Sarah and I had even written our own brief vows to exchange. Because of all this, Mr. Brockman gave away his daughter by pronouncing loudly:

"I, Herbert W. Brockman, on behalf of myself and my wife, do hereby give our daughter, Sarah, in marriage to Mr. Thomas J. Peters, Captain, United States Army Air Force."

When he finished speaking, he placed Sarah's right hand on my left arm and she and I turned and faced Mr. Buddingham. Mr. Buddingham asked each of the witnesses if they were willing to serve as formal witness to our marriage and—thankfully—all said 'Yes'. He then turned to us and directed us to exchange our vows. Sarah read hers to me, but I was so choked up I could hardly read mine to her. When we finished, Mr. Buddingham began speaking. He rattled off several English law regulations governing civil marriage, and he then asked Sarah if she understood and was in compliance with those regulations. She answered "I do."

He then repeated the same to me. I couldn't tell you much of anything about all those regulations, but when he asked me if I understood and was in compliance, I wasn't about to stop him and ask questions! I simply answered "I do."

He then stated that, because we were in compliance with all requirements and regulations, we were now considered under English civil law to be lawfully joined as husband and wife.

I'd never seen a marriage ceremony like that before! But I don't care what it looked like—what it means is—I'm MARRIED TO SARAH!!!!

When Mr. Buddingham made his pronouncement, there was a moment of silence, and then pandemonium broke out! People were on their feet cheering and yelling and whistling. You'd think we'd just won a football championship or something! But it captured EXACTLY how I felt! In fact, I let out a yelp, too! Sarah looked at me and smiled—"I love you, Thomas!"

And I didn't care about propriety or rules or any of that stuff—I swept her into my arms and kissed her like I'd never kissed her before. "I love you, Sarah...Peters!"

* * * * *

That party will go down in the annals of the 336th Fighter Group as a tremendous success. Everyone behaved and everyone had a wonderful, great time. Shortly after the marriage ceremony ended, Mr. and Mrs. Brockman gathered Sarah and me and took us aside.

"Well, Mr. and Mrs. Peters," Mr. Brockman began, "congratulations on your nuptials!"

Sarah and I held tight to each other and smiled and smiled and smiled.

He continued; "As you know, this is wartime and things are very different from normal. Thomas, soon you will be leaving for new military duties in the United States. Your new wife will still be here, wrapping up her affairs and trying desperately to get to the U.S. to be with her husband. Therein lies the rub. One does not simply purchase a ticket and travel merrily out of England."

Sarah and I looked at each other.

"Therefore, Thomas, it is a good thing that your father-in-law is a man of reasonable substance and in good standing with his community. What I am saying is, I have been able to contact various of my friends, and friends of friends, and I have, you might say, 'cashed in' some favors." He handed an envelope to Sarah.

282

She opened it. "Oh, Father!" she gasped.

She showed me the contents: a one-way ticket in the name of Sarah Peters, for a berth on the Queen Mary, sailing on November 13, 1944 from Gourock, Scotland, arriving November 19 in New York, New York, USA. Eureka!!

*   *   *   *   *   *

We left the party late that evening after I'd had a chance to go around and say good-bye to my friends. It was painful for me, because I had trusted my life to these men, and some of them had trusted theirs to me. And some men were even more special: Colonel Martinson, who said nice things about me as he wished me well; Jim Stafford, who was the best pilot I knew and a wonderful friend; Jim Weatherby, who saved my life a dozen times; the ground crew guys, who got shy as we parted; and, finally, Pappy. I know the regulations about relationships between officers and enlisted men, but in my eyes, Pappy should be a General. He and I became so close we're like family. He's a bit of the father I needed to guide me. He made miracles happen for me. I just cannot express the depth of my love—yes, love—for for this indescribable man I call "Pappy".

We spent the precious days of our "honeymoon" at Sarah's flat and, all too soon, it was time for me to pack and leave. It was the hardest thing I have ever done.

Saying goodbye to Sarah hurt more than anything, but at least I knew I'd be seeing her again soon and we would spend our lives together.

Saying goodbye to Reb and Rustler and Jim Weatherby and Major Stafford—and especially Pappy—had been almost unbearable because I doubted I'd ever see them again.

But sometimes, life moves in ways we'd never imagine...

THE END

Author's Request:

Thank you for reading <u>Red Flight, Break!</u> I hope you enjoyed it and I would really appreciate it if you would post a review of this book—I take your comments and insights very seriously. It's easy to post one on the Kindle page for this book and it only takes a couple of minutes.
Thanks!
Roger M.

You might also enjoy the sequel to Red Flight, Break!—<u>Pacific on Fire.</u>

Now available at Amazon Kindle

Made in the USA
Coppell, TX
09 June 2021

57157063R10166